Knowledge Sy
and
Natural Resources

Management, Policy and Institutions in Nepal

Edited by

Hemant R Ojha, Netra P Timsina, Ram B Chhetri
and Krishna P Paudel

International Development Research Centre

Ottawa • Cairo • Dakar • Montevideo • Nairobi • New Delhi • Singapore

FOUNDATION®
B ⊚ ⊚ K S

Delhi • Bangalore • Mumbai • Kolkata • Chennai • Hyderabad

Published by:
Cambridge University Press India Pvt. Ltd.
under the imprint of Foundation Books
Cambridge House
4381/4 Ansari Road
Daryaganj
New Delhi- 110 002

C-22, C-Block, Brigade M.M., K.R. Road, Jayanagar, **Bangalore**- 560 070
Plot No. 80, Service Industries, Shirvane, Sector-1, Nerul, **Navi Mumbai**- 400 706
10, Raja Subodh Mullick Square, 2nd Floor, **Kolkata**- 700 013
21/1 (New No. 49), 1st Floor, Model School Road, Thousand Lights, **Chennai**- 600 006
House No. 3-5-874/6/4, (Near Apollo Hospital), Hyderguda, **Hyderabad**- 500 029

Jointly published by Cambridge University Press India Pvt. Ltd. and International
Development Research Centre.

International Development Research Centre
PO Box 8500
Ottawa, ON KIG 3H9
Canada
www.idrc.ca/info@idrc.ca
ISBN (e-book) 978-1-55250-371-3

Typeset by Amrit Graphics, Shahdara, Delhi 110 032

ISBN: 978-81-7596-563-8 (Paperback)

Published by Manas Saikia for Cambridge University Press India Pvt. Ltd.

Contents

Preface

The book is the outcome of a research project 'Management of Knowledge System in Natural Resources: Exploring Policy and Institutional Framework in Nepal' undertaken by ForestAction Nepal with support from the International Development Research Centre (IDRC), Canada. When we completed the research project with a set of case studies and a review of theories related to knowledge systems and governance and shared the findings with a network of readers, we were excited to get very encouraging feedback. This encouraged us to compile the work as a book so that the empirical findings and insights emerging from the analysis could be disseminated to a wider audience. While preparing the case study reports, we realised that the insights could be potentially beneficial to the policy makers, researchers, planners and field practitioners for developing an understanding of the knowledge systems and their deliberative interface. This idea was materialised with a generous and continued support from IDRC.

We hope that the compilation of case studies on natural resources, in the light of critical and theoretical insights, will help one understand the intricacies of knowledge systems as they relate to governance practices. There is indeed a continuing need for better understanding of the contexts, processes and outcomes of the production of knowledge and its application in various facets of governance of human society. In this context, our main goal of presenting the case studies in this book has been to understand how different systems of knowledge operate in the field of natural resource management, and what factors and conditions affect the process of deliberation among such knowledge systems. We have categorised four key systems of knowledge in Nepal based on the political perspectives and ideologies, which social agents bring in the discourses and practices of natural resource governance. We hope that this approach to analysis goes beyond the on-going debates about local versus scientific, practical versus theoretical and similar categories.

In recent years, we have witnessed that Nepali society is struggling to come out of the tyranny of feudal monarchy and other modes of non-deliberative governance situations. Various movements in the recent past have significantly contributed to pave the path for democracy. Such movements have made the politicians more accountable, transparent and deliberative in democratising, decentralising and devolving the rights to the citizens, including rights to access and control over the natural resources. In this context, how diverse groups of social agents bring in knowledge, and engage deliberately to contribute to the processes of governance is critically important. While our analysis is primarily related to natural resource governance, we believe that the emerging discourse and deliberation of restructuring the Nepali state can also benefit from the findings presented in the book.

As editors, we feel that the case studies can forward fresh perspectives for integrating knowledge and governance in natural resource sectors. First, the four key categories of social agents corresponding to their relatively distinct systems of knowledge are identifiable – techno-bureaucrats, civil society groups, politicians and development agencies. Our main message in this connection is that governance can be understood in terms of the nature and extent of deliberative interface among the knowledge systems of these groups of social agents. While there can be a whole range of differentiated groups within these categories, they are associated with different systems of knowledge and hence bring different perspectives and ideas in the collective action situations of governance. Second, the case studies suggest a number of innovations in the deliberative interface, such as emergence of federation of civil society groups, participatory mechanisms through which technical specialists and natural resource users work together in undertaking research and devising policies, emergence of critical and reflective intellectual practitioners and civil society activists working to bridge technical and civil society knowledge. Third, the constraining impact on deliberative knowledge interface among other systems, primarily as a result of unequal distribution of knowledge resources in the society, has also been identified.

Editing this book has been a process of deliberation among editors and writers who, have different perspectives on how knowledge systems work in the practice of governance. As editors, we have sought to develop theoretically nuanced understanding of how knowledge systems work and how they can improve practices of governance. Our attempt has been on critically reviewing the ideas and concepts applied by the social agents engaged in one or the other systems of knowledge. Through writing workshops and manuscript reviews, we have sought to orient the authors to present case studies in a coherent framework. The authors were also given ample freedom to present their findings in the ways they think appropriate.

The case studies and analytical discussions presented in this book are the outcomes of interactions, discussions and reflections with many people in the research sites, with whom we worked, shared and gained valuable information during the study period. We would like to acknowledge the valuable knowledge contribution of all the people involved. We would like to express sincere gratitude to people of the research sites for their willingness to participate in the discussions and to generate important information and insights. In particular, we appreciate the contribution of local community user groups on forest and irrigation, Federation of Community Forestry User Groups, National Agricultural Research Council, ForestAction Nepal, and Environmental Resources Institute.

Editors
March 2007
Kathmandu

Abbreviations

APP	Agriculture Perspective Plan
APROSC	Agricultural Projects Service Centre
CBO	Community Based Organisation
CBS	Central Bureau of Statistics
CF	Community Forest/Forestry
CFM	Collaborative Forest Management
CFUG	Community Forest User Groups
CMIS	Chattis Mauja Indigenous Irrigation System
CIMMYT	International Maize and Wheat Improvement Centre
DAO	District Administration Office
DFID	Department for International Development
DFO	District Forest Offices
DoF	Department of Forest
FECOFUN	Federation of Community Forestry Users Nepal
FMIS	Farmer-Managed Irrigation System
FSCC	Forestry Sector Coordination Committee
GON	Government of Nepal
LFP	Livelihood and Forestry Programme of DFID
MFSC	Ministry of Forest and Soil Conservation
NARC	Nepal Agricultural Research Council
NARI	National Agricultural Research Institute
NASRI	National Animal Science Research Institute
NGO	Non Governmental Organisation
NNN	Nepal NTFP Network
NTFP	Non Timber Forest Product
OFMP	Operational Forest Management Plan
OP	Operational Plan
ORD	Outreach Research Division
PAL	Participatory Action and Learning
PVS	Participatory Varietals Selection
SDC	Swiss Development Cooperation
TCN	Timber Corporation of Nepal
VDC	Village Development Committees
WATCH	Women Acting Together for Change
WUA	Water Users Association

Glossary of Nepali Words

Badghar A person who is the traditional headman of Tharu community in Nepal.

Bigha A unit of land measurement (equivalent to 0.6772 hectares).

Bighatti The amount of irrigation fee collected per bigha of land in the *Mauja* which varies from *Mauja* to *Mauja*. Water users who do not contribute labour to repair and maintain the main canal are required to pay the irrigation fee.

Chauble Four labourers to be sent per 25 *bighas* of land for the repair and maintenance.

Chaukidar Watchman-cum-messenger in the local context.

Chhattis Mauja A landscape comprising of 36 villages (which were the original command areas).

Gaun Village

Jamindar A *Jamindar* in pre-1961 period in the plains of Nepal was a local landlord who was responsible for the reclamation of the land for the settlements and collection of revenue.

Kattha One-twentieth of a *bigha* (0.0339 hectares).

Khara It is the fine imposed for being absent to contribute the labour for the repair and maintenance.

Kulahai The labour work for the repair and maintenance of the canal.

Kulara One *Kulara* means one labourer per 25 *bighas* of land which is the unit of water allocation between and among the *Maujas* of the irrigation systems.

Mauja A cluster of settlement which roughly corresponds to a village.

Meth Muktiyar	The system level chief staff.
Mohda	The water diversion location from the main canal.
Muktiyar	The chief of a Mauja.
Nath	The measurement of the main canal assigned by the Meth Muktiyar to each *Mauja* for the annual repair and maintenance which is proportionate to the size of its command area.
Panchayat	It was a non-party political system until 1990.
Sabik	It means as usual i.e. one labourer per 25 bighas for repair and maintenance.
Sidhabandhi	It was a repair and maintenance culture of the Tharus with necessary foodstuffs because they had to spend several nights at the improvised camps until the work was over. It was evolved as a function of the long distance of the headwork and the upper part of the canal from the original settlements.
Sohra	Sixteen
Terai	A plain area in the southern part of Nepal.
Treble	Three labourers to be sent per 25 *bighas* of land for repair and maintenance.
Panchayat	The village council until 1990.

1

Knowledge Systems and Deliberative Interface in Natural Resource Governance: An Overiew

Hemant R Ojha, Ram B Chhetri,
Netra P Timsina and Krishna P Paudel

Introduction

This book analyses how diverse knowledge systems operate in the field of natural resource management in Nepal. In order to examine the status of knowledge systems interface and identify the challenges of participatory and deliberative governance of natural resources, the book presents six case studies on forest, agriculture and water governance at different levels – from local community (such as a farmer managed irrigation system) to national research system (such as national agricultural research council) and civil society networking (such as national federation of community forestry users). The over arching issue being addressed in the book is – how questions of equity, efficiency and sustainability in natural resource management are shaped, influenced and determined by deliberative interfaces among diverse knowledge systems associated with diverse groups of social agents engaged in the practice of natural resource governance. Analysis of this issue in the light of empirical evidence and theoretical perspectives can help us draw policy and practical implications for effective knowledge management and social learning in natural resource governance. The book is primarily an analysis of Nepal's experiences and the findings have much wider relevance.

The rationale of the book rests on the need to explore innovative processes and policies to facilitate inclusive, deliberative and equitable governance of resources. Despite recent upsurge of participatory innovations in development actions (Chambers 1994; Chambers 1997) and natural resource management, there is a continuing concern over limited real achievement in terms of local livelihood, economic contributions and natural resource sustainability (Cook and Kothari 2001; Edmunds and Wollenberg 2002; Colfer and Capistrano 2005). In many situations, collective processes of institutions and policy fail to address the opportunities to optimise individual and collective benefits from natural resource governance practices. One of the consequences of such failure is that a vast majority of the world's poor who continue to live at the interface between land, forest and water, often have limited access to such vital resources (Scherr *et al.* 2004; Sunderlin *et al.* 2005). This reality is in part related to how and to what extent diverse groups of social agents, often with different and competing systems of knowledge, deliberate over decisions and practices of natural resource governance. In other words, the challenge of achieving equitable governance of natural resources is related to the ways through which diverse knowledge systems come into deliberative interface to transform or reproduce relations of power and rules of practices.

The challenge of achieving equitable impact from natural resource management is even more critical in view of the expanding frontiers of knowledge and consequent inequity in distribution of knowledge resources at local, national and global levels (Arunachalam 2002; Dufour 2003). As knowledge is expanding exponentially in the global arena, many states with poorly developed knowledge capacity are lagging behind the others in their ability to devise effective policy solutions to a wide range of development problems. The expanding knowledge gaps at all levels have been a concern worldwide, as these gaps are increasingly recognised as being associated with the deteriorating global peace, inequity, environmental degradation and enduring poverty (Arunachalam 2003; Dufour 2003). There is, thus, a direct linkage between equity in sharing benefits from natural resource management and equity in the distribution of knowledge resources.

Involvement of an increasing array of stakeholders in natural resource management has created conditions for conflict and the processes of negotiations will inevitably lead to governance solutions. The emerging diversity of stakeholders has also given rise to the potential for pooling of diverse knowledge traditions in the practice of natural resource governance. But the actual deliberative interface has often been negatively affected by conflicts among different knowledge systems that have developed historically. In Nepal we see that natural resource management practices are mediated by at least four different but overlapping systems of knowledge, viz, techno-bureaucratic knowledge systems, knowledge systems of development agencies, knowledge systems of politicians, and knowledge systems of civil society networks. In the processes of political interaction and deliberation over issues of natural resource governance, we see that these four systems of knowledge underpin the constitution of the four categories of social and political agents. The case studies follow and analyse interaction among these knowledge systems and the ways in which practices of natural resource governance are mediated.

While Nepal's natural resource policies such as community forestry and farmer managed irrigation system have come a long way towards recognising local rights and responsibilities, there are still concerns over achievements of desired outcomes in terms of equity and justice for people. In many parts of the developing world, policies and programmes on participatory natural resource management are just evolving, and there is a significant potential of analysis of knowledge systems driving such practices towards understanding how better results can be achieved. In this context, lessons from the analysis of case studies on natural resource management in Nepal with varied levels of innovations generate useful insights into how deliberative interface of diverse knowledge systems can be strengthened to achieve effective and equitable impact.

The book does not seek to provide a comprehensive assessment of participatory or community based natural resource management practices. It focuses on documenting and interpreting how different groups of social agents engage in various systems of knowledge, and how the processes of deliberation takes place across different groups that draw on diverse systems of knowledge. The next section of this chapter provides a theoretical overview of the issues and concepts related to knowledge, power and governance. Here, we outline how human agency engages and contests in the process of learning and governance. We then present key analytical issues in relation to natural resource management. In the final section of this chapter, we present a comparative overview of the case studies presented in the book.

Knowledge systems and deliberative interface: Key theoretical issues

In this section, we explore the potential of learning and deliberation in the works of key contemporary thinkers such as Habermas, Giddens, Bourdieu, Foucault and Dewey (Key points enumerated on p. 5). The potential of human agency to learn and innovate has significantly expanded since the European Enlightenment in the sixteenth and seventeenth centuries. Since then, science has emerged as a dominant way of understanding social and physical world. The triumph of science which was triggered by experimental methods usually employed in physical world has led to 'overscientisation' of social and political life. Habermas differentiates two domains of learning – technical knowledge and communicative knowledge (Habermas 1971, 1987). While the first is related to how we understand nature to augment human purpose, the second is related to how as humans we understand other each better to create and transform social relationships for greater justice. In

Habermasian language, the second aspect of knowledge is regarded as communicative reason (or communicative rationality) which can potentially be the basis for humans to deliberate across diverse systems of knowledge in order to develop organisations for collective coexistence.

Key theoretical dimensions of learning, power and governance

a. Learning is related to 'agency' dimension of social system (Giddens). Human agency has both discursive as well as doxic elements and learning should be a reflective process to transform doxa (Bourdieu).

b. Human knowledge oriented to understanding nature should be differentiated from human knowledge oriented towards understanding relations between human agents (Habermas).

c. Learning involves both individual as well as collective processes, and collective processes of learning are more crucial to understanding governance and change (Habermas, Dewey).

d. Social agents or 'agencies' are not equipped with equal opportunities to engage in a learning process, and as such learning opportunity itself can be an important cause and effect of social differentiation (Bourdieu).

e. In the contemporary debate between modernity and post-modernity (Habermas versus Foucault and Lyotard), a drive to explore the possibility of human knowledge in desirable social change lies not in either of the extremes but in a critical reconstruction of communicative reason as a basis of social learning (Habermas).

In the post World War II period, western societies sought to assist non-western societies in the process of modernisation and development (Sachs 1993). While such efforts have contributed to physical progress of human beings, they have tended to promote technical knowledge (Scott 1998), at the cost of communicative reason. As a result, socio-political issues are either increasingly being handled by technical experts of government or left to the logic of market, thus minimising the space for deliberation among groups of diverse systems of knowledge. Habermas' reconstruction of rationality has sought to locate the communicative domain of learning away from the technical domain. This has indeed inspired deliberative approaches to governance across a wide variety of collective action situations (Bohman and Rehg 1997; Dryzek 2000). Likewise, another prominent philosopher belonging to the pragmatic school of thought John Dewey's idea that society exists through 'transactional' process of communication and that democracy is itself a learning process (Dewey 1916/1966, 1933/1986; Dewey and Bentley 1949) very much resonates Habermas's conception of communicative democracy. The Pragmatists emphasis on knowledge as practical enterprise parallels Bourdieu's emphasis on practical rationality of human action.

When it comes to communicative interaction or deliberation, the role of human agency is crucial. Giddens has ascribed qualities such as knowledgeability and capabilities on human agency through which they can learn and reconstruct social systems (Giddens 1984). Bourdieu, however, cautions on the excessive optimism of the free will in agency as he considers that human agents are located in structured spaces with pre-reflective dispositions which he calls 'doxa', which inscribes conscious and discursive agency (Bourdieu 1984, 1990, 1998). His view is that discursive knowledge is just a thin tip of a thick doxa (Crossley 2003; Hayward 2004), implying a need for deepening discursive domain of human agents through increased self-reflexivity. In addition, Bourdieu holds that the inherent diversity and differentiation among social agents mean that dominant groups are structurally in better positions to create more holistic and legitimate claims to knowledge through more effective allocation of efforts for action and reflection.

Viewing from the post-structuralist perspective, Michel Foucault (Foucault 1972) considers discourse as the breeding ground for the emergence of social agents. This view widens the scope of deliberative interface, beyond individual reflexivity of social agents who are themselves the products of one or the other discursive formation. For Foucault, discourse creates political subjects along the three axes of human existence

– knowledge, power and ethics. He treats knowledge as embedded in existing power structures. Lyotard, who is even more of a radical postmodernist, has challenged science as an enterprise of experts rather than an objective procedure of representing truth (Lyotard 1993), invoking a relativist epistemology wherein no one can represent no one else. While such poststructural sensibility helps us to think beyond accepted ways of knowing, we cannot ignore the useful roles played by authors and experts when they work in close deliberation with the social agents. For us, the critical question is not whether or not epistemological representation is possible but how holders of different systems of knowledge can arrive at fair practices through negotiation.

Bourdieu's perspective on knowledge should be understood in the universe of practice theory. He has sought to explain social practices in terms of culturally inscribed human agency (habitus), differentiated social domains in which social agents interact (field) and various types of goals which the agents pursue (economic, social, cultural, economic and symbolic capitals). He argues that any social practice results from the interaction among habitus, rules and rewards available in the particular fields, and the structure of access to different types of capitals – social, economic, cultural and symbolic.

Conceptual frameworks for understanding knowledge systems

There are diverse approaches to understanding knowledge systems in diverse contexts of governance. Each of these approaches emerge from particular disciplinary and cultural contexts, and have different degrees of relevance to the field of natural resource management. These are briefly outlined below.

- **Organisational learning:** R M Cyert and J G March (Cyert and March 1963) is considered the foundational work in organisational learning (Easterby-Smith and Lyles 2003; Easterby-Smith 2003). V E Cangelosi and W R Dill (Cangelosi and Dill 1965) revealed the tensions between individuals and organisation, critiquing the work of Cyert and March as being suggestive of models appropriate for established organisations in stable circumstances (Easterby-Smith and Lyles 2003). Special edition of Organisation Science in 1991 significantly popularised the field of organisational learning. J S Brown and P Duguid (Brown and Duguid 1991) laid the foundation for social processes of organisational learning, moving away from personal and psychological emphasis, followed by J Lave (Lave 1988) and others. C Argyris and D Schon (Argyris and Schon 1978) laid the field more clearly, making the critique of rationalist assumptions of Cyert and March, and introducing new concepts (such as 'defensive routines' as the barrier to learning) (Easterby-Smith and Lyles 2003).

- **Learning organisation:** The learning organisation tradition was popularised by P M Senge (Senge 1990), as a practitioner-oriented field of knowledge, emphasising instrumental view (as an aid to technical efficiency) of learning, but playing down social-emotional aspects and political consequences of learning (Garrat 2000).
- **Knowledge management:** Knowledge management (Malhotra and Galletta 2003) seems to take an even more instrumental view of learning, emphasising managed learning using technical tools.
- **Adaptive management:** K N Lee (Lee 1993, 1999) stipulates the idea of adaptive management that considers policies as experiments, and hence emphasises the need for combining monitoring and learning in actual management and collective action situation. Knowledge systems are thus integral to practical and experimental actions, which are designed to solve the immediate human purpose as well.
- **Social learning:** K N Lee (Lee 1993) considers social learning as a combined form of adaptive management and politics – a process of negotiation among diverse groups of social agents. The emphasis here is on exploring how societal institutions can learn, including who learns why and to what extent, under what conditions (Maarleveld and Dabgbégnon 1999; Wollenberg *et al.* 2001; Röling 2002).

- **Adaptive collaborative management (ACM):** ACM blends ideas of learning and social interactions from a diverse range of theoretical sources (Colfer 2005). It builds on Lee's (1993) idea of combining science and politics for social learning in environmental management. It draws on the understanding of the dynamic and complex nature of socio-ecological systems of Gunderson and Holing (Gunderson and Holing 2002). It also draws on the fields of organisational learning and learning organisation to recognise the importance of constant learning in the human interface and creating shared visions of change (Senge 1990, Argyris and Schön 1996). It emphasises making explicit background suppositions of plans and activities, and incorporating a monitoring process tied to the action so that learning does not just become incremental but, seeks to reconstruct perspectives and conceptual frames (Taylor 1998).

- **Action and knowledge/ Participatory Action Research (PAR):** O Fals-Borda and M A Rahman's (Fals-Borda and Rahman 1991) conceptualisation of action and knowledge also seeks to bring learning outside of instrumental domain and engage agencies critically and politically. Here the emphasis is on exploring the emancipatory potential of action and learning, often with critical facilitative support from the agents of change.

- **Participatory learning and action:** Contributions of Paulo Frairie and Robert Chambers (Chambers 1994) have sought to link learning systems of outsiders and insiders in the context of rural development. While Frairie concentrated on developing critical consciousness and conscientisation, Chambers developed methodologies and tools such as participatory rural appraisals to assist outsiders to learn from the local subjects of development.

- **Transformative learning:** Transformative approaches to learning seek to reconstruct perspectives and conceptual frames (Taylor 1998) of human agents as well as develop better understanding of each other through open and deliberative interactions (Forester

1999). These approaches emphasise changes in basic structures of cognition in contrast with incremental approaches to learning.

- **Deliberative processes/deliberative science:** The notion of deliberation is invoked to bring the process and scope of inquiry and learning beyond the domain of expert. Deliberation is considered an opportunity for people to respect each other as moral agents and reach reasonable and legitimate solutions to disputes beyond the confinement of expert inquiry (Forester 1999; Fischer 2003). Since the issues of governance are essentially normative and are not always amenable to objectivist analysis of empirical data, scientific inquiry has sought to 'settle rather than stimulate' the policy debates (Fischer 1998). Deliberative scientific approaches therefore, emphasise on dialogues and negotiation among all pertinent systems of knowledge around the issue of governance.

While a range of approaches to understand and promote knowledge systems are developing in diverse contexts, there is still a paucity of conscious application of such approaches in the field of natural resource governance. Historically, governance of natural resources has been sustained by one or the other forms of knowledge, which actually represent the power and interests of those actors who have been able to influence the practice of natural resource governance. The agrarian society developed what is known now as traditional and indigenous systems of knowledge around diverse types of natural resources, and these systems of knowledge are often contrasted with modern or scientific knowledge, which was promoted by state bureaucracies and modern development projects. While there are studies on how local and scientific knowledge can work together, a key debate in natural resource management is still related to combining indigenous and scientific knowledge systems (Fisher 1989; Chhetri and Pandey 1992; Sillitoe 1998). While many recognise the value of both systems of knowledge in development, debates persist as regards how they can be integrated, and how agents can engage in open deliberation on equal footing to choose and combine local and scientific knowledge systems[1] (Chhetri 1999). Tensions between these tendencies are often manifested in day-to-day practices. We, therefore, take this issue of how local or civil society based knowledge and scientific knowledge can or cannot be integrated in the case studies.

In addition, there are limited analyses of how the interfaces between these two knowledge systems get compounded when the perspectives of political agents and development agencies also come to interact with the former. The other gap is that there are limited analyses on how traditional knowledge resources are also differentially accessible to and controlled by different groups of local people who are themselves divided along multiple axes of hierarchy, such as caste and gender. We argue that natural resource governance cannot be dealt through the dichotomous division between scientific and indigenous knowledge systems; rather we need to explore diverse systems of knowledge triggered by specific configuration of political interests and cultural formations. In the next section, we present diverse systems of knowledge as found in the context of natural resource management in Nepal.

In every human institution, knowledge and power are inextricably linked factors[2], and the treatment of knowledge in isolation gives an incomplete view of learning and innovation system. Power is grounded in diverse dimensions of social class – such as caste, economic assets,

---

1   Rist and Dahdouh-Guebas (2006) identify a range of scenarios through which science and local knowledge can come into interface: *Unacknowledging* (science simply ignores a practice based on local knowledge), *utilitarian* (elements of local knowledge that can be scientifically understood or validated are accepted to increase the stock of scientific knowledge), *paternalistic* (traditional knowledge is conceived of as a starting point that requires 'updating' by science), *neo-colonial* (traditional knowledge and local data are taken from local people and research institutions), *essentialist* (local knowledge is fundamentally better than science, it should not be influenced by Western technology and should have the right to remain as it is), and *intercultural science* (science is aware that it is only one type of knowledge among others, and that knowledge is always embedded in cultural and historical settings. Science and local knowledge can benefit from comprehensive interaction).

2   This is the reciprocal nature of these two words that Foucault titled 'power/knowledge' Allen, B. (1999). 'Power/Knowledge' *Critical Essays on Michel Foucault*. E. K. Racevskis. New York: G.K. Hall & Co.

symbolic capitals (such as social status), gender and ethnicity, to varying degrees. Knowledge-power nexus is enacted, contested and resisted in day-to-day governance practices. Several of the reported tensions in deliberative interface – such as scientific versus indigenous knowledge, theoretical versus practical knowledge – are actually the result of underlying power relations among the social agents.

Knowledge systems interface in natural resource governance

Practices of natural resource governance are shaped by knowledge systems of, and deliberative interfaces among, diverse groups of social agents that tend to vary both in terms of knowledge and other aspects of differentiation. In terms of knowledge-based differentiation, we agree with H R Ojha (Ojha 2006) that four broad categories of social agents claim one or the other forms of stakes in natural resource governance, informed by different systems of knowledge. These are formal political agents, civil society groups, techno-bureaucrats, and development agencies/ professionals (see Fig. 1.1). Depending on the specific contexts of natural resource governance practice, these social agents nurture and utilise different systems of knowledge to learn internally and deliberate with each other.

Besides knowledge based differentiation, other forms of differentiation within and between these categories are also critical to understand the possibility of deliberation in governance. In the unequal and hierarchical social systems of Nepal, knowledge as cultural capital is not equally accessible to all social groupings, and quite often the cultural capital has been a key element of domination in social, political and economic arena. Since constructing knowledge requires engagement in action, reflection, networking and sharing (Dewey and Bentley 1949), agencies that have access to time and resources to such processes are in a better position to learn. This applies to the condition of social inequality from a small community to global system.

The figure below introduces the four different categories of social agents with different systems of knowledge.

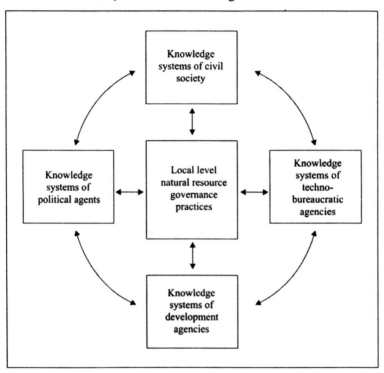

Fig. 1.1 Four types of knowledge systems interface in local level natural resource management practices

First, formal political agency (or habitus) is enacted by the groups of people who think that it is important to engage in the affair of the state and the government, and to lead or mobilise people in that matter. They generally organise themselves as political groups (such as a political party). This type of agency emerges in political fields in which certain groups of people acquire dispositions, interests and recognition to represent and rule communities, groups, organisations and institutions. They acquire significant levels of positional power which privileges their perspectives and ideas in decision making processes.

The history of Nepal's political field shows that over the course of time certain groups have captured state power and alienated civil society from exercising power and authority over the affairs of the state. The governance of state has been an extension of feudal regime developed in the context of small principalities and agrarian landlordism, which often followed a dynastic line of succession, leaving the civil society agents as ruled subjects. While Nepal has recently witnessed strong resisitance against feudalism demanding democracy, the political parties which led political movements are yet to be internally democratic and deliberative in integrating diverse systems of knowledge. This means that knowledge systems of political agents are guided more by the power legacies of feudalism than the ideals of deliberative knowledge interface among diverse systems of knowledge.

In natural resource governance in Nepal, political agency engages in the formulation of policy as well as enacting governance at different levels. Leadership positions in natural resource governance institutions such as Community Forest User Groups, Water User Groups are taken up by formal political agents who bring feudalistic tendency in deliberative processes of forest governance. This agency is vertically differentiated into groups at community level to political leaders at national level.

The second system of knowledge brought to deliberative interface in natural resource governance is the one nurtured in the civil society, which is a sphere that stands distinct from the apparatus of the state (Habermas 1996). Normatively speaking, civil society is concerned with any public policy decision affecting civil life, although the level of concerns vary significantly. Given the historically constituted feudalistic nature of Nepali state (Bista 1991), civil society and its knowledge system has had very limited interface in the governance of natural resources. While local level civil society has managed natural resource systems in many parts of the country traditionally, often with rich indigenous knowledge, there has been limited recognition of this knowledge system in formal policy making and local level governance. The problem of civil society knowledge interface is further compounded by the social differentiation in terms of caste, class, ethnicity and gender. As a result, the seemingly rich repertoire of indigenous knowledge in natural resource management is controlled by and accessible to local feudal lords and upper echelons of local civil society. What is even more critical is that those who have been marginalised are led to believe in their fate or *Karma* for their success, achievements and failures in life (Bista 1991). This gives limited motivation for active learning and generation of knowledge that can help these groups to negotiate natural resource governance decisions. The potential of civil society to come into effective deliberative interface thus depends on how and to what extent their own internal knowledge system is organised, allowing the representation of disadvantaged civil groups.

The third system of knowledge in natural resource governance is nurtured by techno-bureaucratic habitus, which emerges from the field that organises, facilitates, enforces, and enacts public decisions by creating professionalised organisational forms using top-down control mechanisms. This habitus includes technical experts, bureaucrats and professionals who have a tendency to view complex social realities in simpler and linear disciplinary frames (Fisher 1990). They tend to blend positional power with disciplinary orientations to pursue their interests often in the name of discharging public functions and responsibilities. In the wake of technological progress and modernisation, there is a strong belief in and wider recognition of such technocratic approaches in the field of natural resource management whether it be in research, policy or practices. Technocratic dispositions tend to instrumentalise learning and social change using technical reason, away from the public domain of all concerned. Techno-bureaucratic orthodoxy in Nepal considers itself a *hakim* (the boss) of people and authentic producer of knowledge (Ojha 2006). Deliberative possibility lies in promoting social learning of citizens in public problems (Reich 1989; Forester 1999).

Finally, developmentalist or *vikase* habitus brings relatively distinct systems of knowledge. The defining feature of this habitus is that it has a concern that people are undeveloped, and some kind of external intervention and support is needed. Over the past 50 years of development history in Nepal, an entire category of such people has emerged who commonly share that developmentalism is the only way to liberate Nepali society. They are at different social locations – from community to national agencies of development with a common frame of mind that development actions can liberate society from poverty, injustice and underdevelopment. In the recent years, the notion of development has been highly conflated and is more rhetorical than in practice, and this is established by recent upsurge of critical research and reflections on the failure of development practice in Nepal (Shrestha 1998; Pandey 1999; Blaikie *et al.* 2002) as well as internationally (Ferguson 1994; Escobar 1995; Harris 2001). In the recent years, more deliberative developmental processes are spearheaded by intellectuals, development activists, human rights workers, and civil society network activists who seek to challenge the mainstream discourses and practices of development and advocate for devolution, decentralisation, participatory governance and protection of local people's rights over natural resources.

The central issue related to the functioning of the knowledge systems in natural resource management is about the possibility of deliberation among diverse systems of knowledge and perspectives held by the four primary groups of human agency described above. While the policy and practice of natural resource governance is enacted through knowledge and political interfaces among all the four categories of agency to varying degrees in various ways, the problem lies in the persistent divergence of perspectives and difficulty in achieving negotiated outcomes. From the perspective of deliberative governance (as a strategy of resolving the conflict among different knowledge systems), the case studies presented in this book identify problems of domination in deliberative processes involving the four key knowledge systems.

Overview of case studies

We investigated knowledge systems at different levels (local, sub-national, and national), different sectors (forest, agriculture, irrigation), and different institutions (government, donors, civil society and local communities) (see Table 1.1). At the local level, emphasis was on understanding how community groups, households, individuals, wealth categories including gender and ethnicity engage in and benefit from, managing knowledge. In doing this, four Forest User Groups (FUGs) and two Water User Groups (WUGs) were selected at the local level to represent three distinct ecological zones - Terai, Middle Hills and Mountains of Nepal. At sub-national level, contribution of Federation of Community Forestry Users, Nepal (FECOFUN) in relation to democratising power and knowledge dynamics has been documented. At the national level, Nepal Agricultural Research Council and the case of community forestry inventory policy has been studied.

The cases together provide diverse scenarios of deliberative interface among diverse knowledge systems. The cases reveal that primary contestation is between civil society and techno-bureaucratic knowledge systems, mediated to varying degrees by the knowledge systems of development agencies and political agents.

The case of NARC presents deliberative interface between civil society knowledge of farmers and techno-bureaucratic knowledge of agricultural scientists. We have evidences of both improving deliberation as well as continued domination of scientific knowledge. The case of community forestry inventory presents an interface between civil society knowledge of forest users and techno-bureaucratic knowledge of technical forestry staff of the government Department of Forest. The cases of Lo Manthang and FECOFUN are perhaps at the other end of the spectrum. In both the cases, the NRM institutions are primarily sustained by civil society led knowledge systems, which have challenged the irrelevant elements and approaches of techno-bureaucratic knowledge and incorporated the relevant and useful aspects of the latter. The case of Lo Manthang suggests that social agents who live as a small community with rich traditions and cultural resources actually promote learning and innovation as part of their life. The case of FECOFUN demonstrates how citizens can be organised to challenge and transform the technocratic learning approaches dominant in the forestry sector.

Table 1.1   Case studies and summary characteristics

Case	Summary Characteristics
NARC	• Primarily a deliberative interface between agricultural scientists and farmers. • Deliberative processes dominated by techno-bureaucratic and fatalistic mindsets of government research scientists and fatalistic thinking of civil society. The research system has limited influence of both political and development actors. • Presence of interface between indigenous and scientific knowledge systems.
FECOFUN	• Primarily a deliberative interface between civil society network and forestry experts and bureaucrats. • Presence of civil society challenge to forestry techno-bureaucrats. • Significantly influenced by the ideas and resources of development agencies. • Fostering knowledge networking for civil society advocacy. • Providing innovative deliberative platforms between civil society and techno-bureaucratic knowledge systems.
Chhattis Mauja	• An institution sustained by knowledge of local civil society. • Limited influence of development agents. • A large infrastructure sustained by indigenous knowledge, increasingly integrated with modern technology.
Lo Manthang	• A system of irrigation sustained by local civil society knowledge. • Encounter between techno-bureaucratic knowledge and civil society knowledge systems. • Deliberative innovation in integrating civil society and scientific knowledge systems.
CFUGs	• Techno-bureaucrats driving forest management planning and implementation processes. • Meaningful interaction between local civil society and development NGOs. • Critical facilitation by development NGOs contributing to improved deliberation and recognition of civil society knowledge and perspectives.
Forest Inventory	• Influence of forest techno-bureaucracy over local control of resources. • Civil society resistance to non-deliberative construction of forest policy instrument. • Deliberation is impeded due to power imbalance between civil society agents and techno-bureaucrats, as well as non-transparent collusion of local political elites and bureaucrats for their own interests.

The case of *Chhattis Mauja* represents a situation in which originally a civil society led knowledge system is being increasingly married with scientific knowledge system to address issues of efficiency in irrigation management. Action learning processes in four CFUGs demonstrate a situation in which a group of intellectuals and activists promoted transformative processes of learning – among themselves and the local villagers.

References

Argyris, C. and D. Schon (1978). *Organizational Learning: A Theory of Action Perspective.* Reading, Mass: Addison-Wesley.

Argyris, C. and D. Schön (1996). *Organizational Learning II: Theory, Method and Practice.* Reading, Mass: Addison-Wesley.

Arunachalam, S. (2002). 'The Global Research Village: A View from Periphery'. Commissioned paper, IDRC.

Bista, D. B. (1991). *Fatalism and Development: Nepal's Struggle for Modernisation.* Calcutta: Orient Longman.

Blaikie, P., J. Cameron and D. Seddon (2002). Understanding 20 Years of Change in West-Central Nepal: Continuity and Change in Lives and Ideas. *World Development,* 30 (7): 1255–1270.

Bohman, J. and W. Rehg, (eds.) (1997). Deliberative Democracy: Essays on Reason and Politics. Massachusetts and London: The MIT Press.

Bourdieu, P. (1984). *Distinction: A Social Critique of the Judgment of Taste.* Cambridge, Mass: Harvard University Press.

Bourdieu, P. (1990). *In Other Words: Essays towards Reflexive Sociology.* Cambridge: Polity Press in association with Blackwell.

Bourdieu, P. (1998). *Practical Reason: On the Theory of Action.* Cambridge: Polity.

Brown, J. S. and P. Duguid (1991). Organisational Learning and Communities of Practice: Toward a Unified View of Working, Learning and Innovation. *Organization Science,* 2 (1): 40–57.

Cangelosi, V. E. and W. R. Dill (1965). Organisational Learning: Observations toward a Theory. *Administrative science quarterly,* 10 (2): 175–203.

Chambers, R. (1994). Participatory Rural Appraisal (PRA): Analysis of Experience. *World Development,* 22 (9): 1253–1268.

Chambers, R. (1997). *Whose Reality Counts? Putting the Last First.* London: Intermediate Technology.

Chhetri, R. B. (1999). The Rhetoric and Realities of People's Participation in Conservation and Development in Nepal. In R. B. Chhetri and O. P. Gurung (eds.), *Anthropology and Sociology of Nepal - Cultures, Societies, Ecology and Development* (192–211). Kathmandu: Sociological/Anthropological Society of Nepal (SASON).

Chhetri, R. B. and T. R. Pandey (1992). User Group Forestry in the Far-Western Region of Nepal: Case Studies Form Baitadi and Accham Districts. Kathmandu: ICIMOD.

Colfer, C. J. P. (2005). The Complex Forest-Communities, Uncertainty and Adptive Collaborative Management. Washington and Bogor: RFF and CIFOR.

Colfer, C. J. P. and D. Capistrano, (eds.) (2005). *The Politics of Decentralisation – Forests, Power and People.* London and Sterling: EARTHSCAN.

Cook, B. and U. Kothari (2001). 'The Case for Participation as Tyranny', In B. Cook and U. Kothari (eds.), *Participation: The New Tyranny* (1–15). London and New York: Zed.

Crossley, N. (2003). From Reproduction to Transformation: Social Movement Fields and the Radical Habitus. *Theory, Culture and Society,* 20 (6): 43–68.

Cyert, R. M. and J. G. March (1963). *A Behavioral Theory of the Firm.* Englewood Cliff, NJ: Prentice-Hall.

Dewey, J. (1916/1966). *Democracy and Education: An Introduction to the Philosophy of Education.* New York : The Free Press.

Dewey, J. (1933/1986). *How We Think: A Restatement of the Relation of Reflective Thinking to the Educative Process.* Boston: D C Heath and Company.

Dewey, J. and A. F. Bentley (1949). *Knowing and the Known.* Westport, Connecticut: Greenwood Press.

Dryzek, J. S. (2000). *Deliberative Democracy and Beyond: Liberals, Critics, and Contestations.* Oxford: Oxford University Press.

Dufour, P. (2003). 'Future of Knowledge for Development Strategies: Moving from Rhetoric to Reality.' Commissioned Paper, IDRC.

Easterby-Smith, M. and M. Lyles (2003). Introduction: Watersheds of Organisational Learning and Knowledge Management. In: Easterby-Smith, Mark and Lyles and Marjorie (eds.), *The Blackwell Handbook of Organizational Learning and Knowledge Management.* London: The Blackwell Publishing Ltd.

Easterby-Smith, Mark and Lyles and Marjorie (2003). Organisational Learning and Knowledge Management: Agendas for Future Research. In: Easterby-Smith, Mark and Lyles and Marjorie (eds.), *The Blackwell Handbook of Organizational Learning and Knowledge Management* (639–652). London: The Blackwell Publishing Ltd.

Edmunds, D. and E. Wollenberg (2002). *Disadvantaged Groups in Multistakeholder Negotiations.* Indonesia: CIFOR.

Escobar, A. (1995). *Encountering Development: The Making and Unmaking of The Third World.* Princeton, NJ: Princeton University Press.

Fals-Borda, O. and M. A. Rahman (1991). *Action and Knowledge: Breaking the Monopoly with Participatory Action-Research*. London: Intermediate Technology Publications, The Apex Press.

Ferguson, J. (1994). *The Anti-Politics Machine: Development, De-politicisation and Bureaucratic Power in Lesotho*. Minneapolis: University of Minnesota Press.

Fischer, F. (1998). Beyond Empiricism: Policy Inquiry and Post Positivist Perspective. *Policy Studies*, 26 (1): 129–146.

Fischer, F. (2003). *Reframing Public Policy: Discursive Politics and Deliberative Practices*. Oxford and New York: Oxford University Press.

Fisher, F. (1990). *Technocracy and the Politics of Expertise*. Newbury Park, CA: Sage Publications.

Fisher, R. J. (1989). *Indigenous Systems of Common Property Forest Management in Nepal*. Honolulu: Environment and Policy Institute.

Forester, J. (1999). *The Deliberative Practitioner: Encouraging Participatory Planning Processes*. Cambridge, Massachusetts and London: The MIT Press.

Foucault, M. (1972). *The Archaelogy of Knowledge*. London: Tavistock.

Garrat, B. (2000). *The Learning Organization: Developing Democracy at Work*. London: Profile Books.

Giddens, A. (1984). *The Constitution of Society: Outline of the Theory of Structuration*. Cambridge and Oxford: Polity Press.

Gunderson, L. H. and C. S. Holing, (eds.) (2002). *Panarchy: Understanding Transformation in Human and Natural Systems*. Washington D.C: Island Press.

Habermas, J. (1971). *Knowledge and Human Interests*. Boston: Beacon Press.

Habermas, J. (1996). *Between Facts and Norms: Contributions to a Discourse Theory of Law and Democracy*. Masachusetts: MIT Press.

Habermas, J. (1987). *The Theory of Communicative Action: Life World and System-a Critique of Functionalist Reason* (Vol 2). Polity Press.

Harris, J. (2001). *Depoliticizing Development: The World Band and Social Capital*. London: Anthem Press.

Hayward, C. R. (2004). Doxa and Deliberation. *Critical Review of International Social and Political Philosophy*, 7 (1): 1–24.

Lave, J. (1988). *Cognition in Practice: Mind, Mathematics and Culture in Everyday Life*. Cambridge: Cambridge University Press.

Lee, K. N. (1993). *Compass and Gyroscope: Integrating Science and Politics for the Environment*. Washington D.C.: Island Press.

Lee, K. N. (1999). Appraising Adaptive Management. *Conservation Ecology,* 3 (3).

Lyotard, J. F. (1993). *Political Writings*. London: University College London Press.

Maarleveld, M. and C. Dabgbégnon (1999). Managing Natural Resources: A Social Learning Perspective. *Agriculture and Human Values*, 16 (3): 267–280.

Malhotra, Y. and D. F. Galletta (2003). *Role of Commitment and Motivation in Knowledge Management Systems Implementation: Theory, Conceptualization and Measurement of Antecedent Success.* Proceedings of the 36th Hawaii International Conference on Systems Sciences.

Ojha, H. (2006). Techno-Bureaucratic Doxa and Challenges for Deliberative Governance: The Case of Community Forestry Policy and Practice in Nepal. *Policy and Society*, 25 (2): 151–204.

Pandey, D. R. (1999). *Nepal's Failed Development: Reflections on the Mission and Maladies.* Kathmandu: Nepal South Asia Centre.

Reich, R. B. (ed.) (1988). *The Power of Public Ideas.* Cambridge, MA: Ballinger.

Rist, S. and F. Dahdouh-Guebas (2006). Ethnosciences - a Step Towards the Integration of Scientific and Indigenous Forms of Knowledge in the Management of Natural Resources for the Future. *Environment, Development and Sustainability*, 8: 467–493.

Röling, N. (2002). Beyond the Aggregation of Individual Preferences: Moving from Multiple to Distributed Cognition in Resource Dilemmas. In C. Leeuwis, and Pyburn R (eds.), *Wheelbarrows Full of Frogs. Social Learning in Rural Resource Management.* The Netherlands: Koninklijke Van Gorcum, Assen.

Sachs, W. (1993). *The Development Dictionary: A Guide to knowledge as Power.* Editorial Introduction, pp. 1–7. New Delhi: Orient Longman.

Scherr, S. J., A. White and D. Kaimowitz (2004). A New Agenda for Forest Conservation and Poverty Reduction. Washington D C: Forest Trends, CIFOR and IUCN.

Scott, J. (1998). *Seeing Like a State: How Certain Schemes to Improve Human Condition Have Failed.* New Haven and London: Yale University Press.

Senge, P. M. (1990). *The Fifth Discipline: The Art and Practice of the Learning Organization.* London: Century Business.

Shrestha, N. R. (1998). *In the Name of Development: A Reflection on Nepal.* Kathmandu: Educational Enterprises Limited.

Sillitoe, P. (1998). The Development of Indigenous Knowledge-a New Applied Anthropology. *Current Anthropology*, 39 (2): 223–252.

Sunderlin, W. D., A. Angelsen, B. Belcher, P. Burgers, R. Nasi, L. Santoso and S. Wunder (2005). Livelihoods, Forests, and Conservation in Developing Countries: An Overview. *World Development*, 33 (9): 1383.

Taylor, E. W. (1998) *The Theory and Practice of Transformative Learning-a Critical Review.* Columbus, Ohio: The Ohio State University.

Wollenberg, E., D. Edmunds, L. Buck and S. Brodt, (eds.) (2001). *Social Learning in Community Forests.* CIFOR and the East-West Centre.

2

Agricultural Technology Development in Nepal: Critical Assessment from Knowledge System Perspective

Netra P Timsina and Hemant R Ojha

Introduction

Agriculture has been the foundation of Nepalese economy and has been part of the culture, knowledge system and way of life of Nepali society for centuries. Today approximately 80 per cent of the population depends on agriculture for subsistence. Realising the importance of agriculture as a means of livelihood, for majority of the people, the government began planned interventions in the agriculture sector in the 1950s. Technological inputs particularly the introduction of improved varieties of crops and their trials were the initial outside interventions in agriculture. The focus on the production of crops under the influence of dominant discourse of science and technology has created an inherent conflict between the scientific and indigenous knowledge systems.

The government of Nepal developed the Agriculture Perspective Plan (APP) in 1995. The objectives of APP were to reduce the proportion of population living below the poverty line and to specifically include rural poor women in that process through agricultural interventions. It was an action plan, which identified four key priority areas of input and output. Priority inputs included irrigation, fertiliser, technology, roads and power, whereas priority outputs included livestock, high value crops, agribusiness and forestry (APP 1995; JMA and APROSC 1998). In line with the APP, the sole objective of the Tenth Plan (2002–2007) of Nepal was set 'to bring about a remarkable and sustainable reduction in the poverty level'. The Tenth Plan focused on two major areas for the agriculture sector:

a.   to increase agricultural production, productivity, and income for food security and poverty reduction

b.   develop local and export market opportunities (NPC 2002).

The Agricultural Policy 2004 further elaborated the importance of agricultural production for poverty reduction in Nepal. Nepal Agricultural Research Council (NARC) has been the main national institution to carry out research activities for increasing agricultural productivity and production by generating appropriate agro-technologies.

This chapter takes NARC as a case and builds the analysis around the issues of knowledge system in agriculture technology development in Nepal. It briefly introduces the objectives and functions of NARC. It then documents the views of scientists working for NARC on policies, institutions and technology development. It also presents the perceptions of farmers on NARC and agriculture technology development. The discussion then shifts to issues of knowledge system in agriculture technology in Nepal. Equity, gender and marginalisation of indigenous knowledge systems have been some of the prominent issues in the present practice of agriculture-technology development. The key finding is that learning system within NARC and between other stakeholders appears to be weak and hence, there is a need to strengthen collaboration between stakeholders in order to enhance deliberative interface between scientists and farmers.

An overview of Nepal Agricultural Research Council

The concepts, theories, tools and techniques developed at international level and subsequent changes in development paradigms (Yapa 1993; Chambers 1997) have an influence on developing national agricultural policies and technologies all over the world. The evolution and development of NARC system was highly influenced by international agricultural knowledge system and the institutional structures were also shaped accordingly. NARC is an autonomous apex body at the national level to undertake agricultural research activities to increase agricultural productivity and production by generating appropriate agro-technologies suitable to various agro-ecological zones for the country's diversified crops like cereals, grain legumes, oilseeds, cash/industrial crops, horticulture, livestock, swine, avian and fisheries (NARC 2001). It was established in 1991 under the authority of Article 19 of the Nepal Agricultural Research Council Act 1991.

Major functions of NARC include generating cost-effective and client oriented improved technologies, processing them in varied sequences at research stations and farms, verifying them in farmers' conditions through outreach research programmes and disseminating the proven technologies through various extensions and transfer agents (NARC 2001). The NARC has been focusing on four major technologies, namely, generating technologies for subsistence (technologies for major food crops for food security), commercialisation (technologies for crops having market scopes), rural employment, and natural resource management in relation to environmental sustainability (NARC 2001).

NARC comprises separate wings of 14 national commodity research programmes, four regional agricultural research stations and three units of agriculture environment, post harvest and biotechnology (NARC 2001). It has two institutions under its umbrella: the National Agricultural Research Institute (NARI) and the National Animal Science Research Institute (NASRI). While NARI deals mainly with research on agricultural and horticultural crops and related activities, NASRI deals with livestock and fishery research activities in the country. NARC is one of the biggest research organisations in the country in terms of the number of human resources engagement. It has a total of more than 1800 staff working in different research stations and institutes. Out of the total, more than 300 are working as scientists, and about 900 as technical staff (NARC 2001).

As mentioned earlier, developing improved varieties is the major focus of NARC. It has released more than 100 varieties of fruits, vegetables and food crops. NARC has Outreach Research Division (ORD) to test the suitability of new technology in a farmer's domain. The main objective of ORD is to carry out on-farm participatory technology development activities and enhance linkages with various stakeholders. It also aims to generate new cost-effective adaptive technologies that are suitable to farmers' biophysical and socio-economic conditions. Presently, NARC has more than 50 outreach research sites located in various regions and districts in the country. NARC has adopted a variety of participatory selection[3] (PVS) process and participatory plant breeding, in which farmers are also involved in selecting the varieties of crops.

Different perspectives on agriculture technology development

Scientists' perspectives

The scientists of NARC have made a number of changes in functions, competencies and stakeholder collaborations in relation to generating agricultural technologies. Scientists at NARC believe that NARC has improved its research capacity by developing competent human resources as well as by forging collaborations with civil society partners including Non Governmental Organisations (NGOs) which bring in civil perspectives and enhance knowledge partnership in agricultural

---

[3]   Five replications are made in farmers filed for each technology and crops. There may be a number of crops and number of technologies for each crop. Moreover, in addition to the research work, ORD launches some other associated activities in order to popularise the technology which involves many farmers.

development. Scientists have appreciated the importance of incorporating local knowledge and partnership with local communities. During the interviews for this research, scientists themselves admitted that knowledge base of almost all the scientists in their organisation comes from the school and university based education, and recognises the significance of the indigenous knowledge system which has existed with the community and farmers for generations. Based on the traditional/indigenous knowledge systems, farmers are capable of selecting appropriate varieties that are suitable for their ecological and socio-economic domain. The scientists through planning and consultation meetings at village, district and regional levels have sought to pool the knowledge of farmers to develop appropriate variety selection technologies. For example, the participatory variety selection is one of the effective approaches which combine the knowledge of scientists and the local people. However, the challenge is to fully recognise the value of indigenous knowledge system while developing technologies, since the approach to developing new technology was found to be highly dominated by the professional interests of scientists.

Regarding communication of technology, scientists mentioned that most effective source of technology dissemination is farmer-to-farmer exchange and sharing. Also, NARC stations and farms, demonstration plots and exchange visits are found to be important means of dissemination. At the same time, they admitted that there is limited monitoring of technology adoption and limited documentation of farmer-to-farmer spread of technology, which resulted in a lack of information on the status of the effectiveness of the technology generated.

Scientists at NARC have mixed reactions about their working environment in relation to knowledge production and dissemination. Some scientists appreciate pluralistic notions of knowledge and partnership in agricultural development of Nepal and also recognise the socio-economic and cultural complexities of farmers in adopting new technologies. However, others appear to be reluctant to accept the knowledge of the farmers as the authentic knowledge in agricultural development. The expertise and function of scientists is structured around specific products or species rather than at a system of knowledge involving production and dissemination. A senior scientist in NARC said, "I am a wheat person, and do not know much about rice, though I need to keep changing my work from commodity to commodity".

Lack of coordination between scientists and extension workers is a major issue in relation to building an effective mechanism for deliberative knowledge interface between scientists and local farmers. Extension workers at the district level commented that NARC research activity still lacks adequate participatory considerations to generate knowledge useful for the local farmers. One of the extension workers in Eastern Terai district of Saptari commented, "participatory research is not conducted by the NARC yet. It has started research in the name of outreach but the principles of participation are hardly applied in research activities. Here, the farmers and extension workers are involved only for ritual". He further claimed that suggestions given by the extension workers are never utilised in the research operations.

Some other scientists felt that technicians were still considered as second grade professionals as compared to the administrators of the same hierarchy. One of the senior scientists commented, "administrators still consider themselves that they are more powerful, although they have little analytical knowledge". However, they also mentioned a number of challenges of the NARC system. Internal cooperation among the staff working with the NARC is weak, and collaboration with related agencies is even more problematic. The majority of the scientists interviewed were happy with the early promotion in NARC system. They also appreciated that NARC is less hierarchical than Agriculture Ministry and its Departments value the opportunities to be involved in academic activities.

Although the policies of NARC have accepted the role of NGOs and private sector in agricultural research systems, the scientists have mixed reactions to the partnership with NGOs and private sector. While some scientists have appreciated the collaboration between NARC and

NGOs and private sectors, some other scientists appear to be reluctant to accept the knowledge with the NGOs as valid knowledge. They raise the issue that the nature of work which NARC does, demands rigorous scientific skills and knowledge which most of the NGOs lack. Nevertheless, some scientists appreciated the NGOs work as often being more effective than NARC in delivering services at local level.

Farmers' perspectives

In interactions with different wealth categories, gender and ethnic groups during the field visit of the study, a gap was observed between the farmers and agricultural scientists in interpreting the high yielding technologies. Farmers interpret by reflecting upon their experiences. A group of poor farmers responded about the high yielding varieties as follows:

"We have heard that there were improved seeds of cereals and vegetables that give more production. But the seeds were too expensive and beyond our capacity to buy. We thought that those seeds were only for rich farmers who can afford them" (A farmer in a group meeting, Darbesha, Morang, 2003).

Similarly, in a group meeting of farmers in eastern Terai (Jhoda Hat, Morang) a farmer mentioned:

"Before 10–15 years, we used to keep all seeds in our home that we required for next season (cereals, vegetables and oilseeds). However, after the introduction of high yielding seeds, we started to depend on market and it was easy to buy seeds from market than storing at home. We almost lost our indigenous varieties of vegetable seeds. But, after certain period of time, the improved seeds started to decline in productivity. By now, we have already lost our system of storing seed and related knowledge. Moreover, the improved varieties demand high external inputs to the level that we cannot afford. The intervention of improved varieties as new technology has increased our cost of cultivation without having significant benefits from it".

However, the farmers who have sizable land to cultivate have different views on high yielding varieties. Some of the farmers near the outreach site of NARC in central Terai district of Nawalparasi expressed that after the introduction of high yielding maize variety, the production has more than doubled. For example, the local variety used to give a production of approximately 3000 kilograms per hectare, whereas the hybrid variety yields a production of approximately 7500 kilograms. Another benefit of the hybrid seeds is that it takes shorter period to mature, so that one more crop can be grown in the same season. However, there is increased problem of diseases, insects and pests infesting the crops.

Similarly, many farmers discussed about the practice of knowledge sharing and its usefulness in variety selection. Maniram Chaudhari from Nawalparasi said that the government agencies have no capacity to provide sufficient services to farmers and they learned about these services from mutual sharing such as meetings and interactions. He also revealed that the farmers share knowledge and skills with each other. The crop varieties provided by the agriculture office are usually cultivated for one year and majority of the farmers discontinue from the second year. This is mainly due to the low quality of the seeds. According to them, the agriculture office distributed a variety of rice to the farmers a few years back, but the performance of the crop was not satisfactory. One of the farmers commented, "all varieties provided by the agriculture office do not necessarily give good performance as the technicians do not have knowledge of the location".

An interaction with farmers of Hanumannagar, an outreach site of NARC in Saptari, revealed their dissatisfaction regarding the working approach of the outreach station. They felt that the outreach research was mainly focused on the verification trial of technologies developed by the research stations of NARC. For this purpose, some of the farmers were involved in the research trial as local partners. They were asked to express their needs and problems many times, but these were never operationalised. Instead, the research trials were based on the interests of researchers and research institutions rather than addressing the farmers' needs and interests. A farmer in the outreach research site stated, "we were asked about our need and priority of research in pre-research workshop and we provided various suggestions and options. But these were never operationalised". According to him, a local hot pepper species is very much popular in that locality and their interest was to expand its cultivation. But this was not considered to be the priority of NARC.

Some of the rich farmers have different interests than the ordinary farmers. Umesh Kumar Mehta, a rich farmer of the village, says:

"Although some varieties of potato tested on the outreach station appeared to be outstanding and we are cultivating them, the research and even the extension is unable to fulfill our demands for seed. We have to fetch improved seeds of cereals and vegetables from the neighboring country, India. Our demand is towards high yielding varieties even if they are input intensive."

For rich farmers, the productivity of the crop was the main concern. They wanted to cultivate high yielding varieties, preferably hybrids, even if they incurred more input costs.

However, the interests of resource weak poor farmers appear to be different than the rich farmers. Ramsewak Mehta, a poor farmer expresses, "we want more production from our agricultural land with low cost. Almost all the high yielding varieties are high input demanding that we can not afford to buy the input". The statement above also demonstrates their need for low cost technologies and their dissatisfaction with the high input technologies. They wish their local technologies to be researched and improved at the outreach sites. Likewise, Krishna Dev Mehta, president of a farmers' group 'Lotus Brihad Bagbani Samuha' thinks that research should focus on the locally available resources and technologies which are proven better suited to the local situation.

Most of the poor farmers interviewed were interested in raising small livestock and vegetable production, which do not need large investment and efforts. Although some components of small livestock and vegetable production are included in the NARC's research program, it is not a priority. It means that NARC's researches on technology development are not planned consciously in addressing the problems of resource poor farmers. Most of the technology generated by NARC are absorbed/adapted by the rich farmers, as the poor farmers have not been able to afford the inputs for high yielding varieties. The poor own very small parcels of land, as a result, they cannot easily adopt new technologies that involve greater input costs. The evidences show that the technology developments in high yielding varieties have benefited some urban areas or the road heads because of the market opportunities for the products. For example, most of the off-season vegetables and other cash crop varieties developed by NARC are grown near the urban areas. The issue of equity is particularly important in the case of Nepal which is characterised by chronic poverty, social injustice and inequality and conflict. Given the hierarchical structure of Nepalese society, the technology generated so far benefit the rich and dominant ethnic groups. Laxmi Devi Mehta, a female farmer in the outreach research site said, "we, women from Terai do not know much about the technology generated form NARC that is useful for us".

Emerging issues in agriculture technology development: Whose knowledge counts?

The discussions in the above sections reveal that the knowledge system in NARC is organised along disciplinary lines and agricultural commodities. The key knowledge development function of NARC scientists is to improve crop varieties and animals through scientific experiments and methods. The scientists tend to work in isolation rather than in a holistic and integrated way in knowledge production. Although they have developed low input technology such as zero tillage, the basis of the technology generation is guided mainly by their scientific wisdom that originates from the research stations and academic institutions. It is evident from the field study that pure technological research without adequate considerations of the perceptions and constraints of resource poor farmers can have limited impact on changing the livelihoods of the poor. The present model of technology development does not consider the structure of social relations and system of social practices through which technologies filter and become accessible to people with limited land and other resources. Interpersonal socio-economic differences play important roles in determining who benefits with the technological innovations.

Besides, scientists seem to regard themselves as the formal, legal and authentic source of knowledge. Interactions with some scientists during this study reinforces the idea that they still have strong sense of themselves as the only legitimate knowledge authorities in agricultural sector. Generally, they did not seem to appreciate the local context specific research carried out by small-scale research agencies such as local farmers' networks and professional NGOs. This indicates the continued preoccupation of bureaucratic power and the scientists' emphasis on technical rationality in generating new knowledge.

In recent years, there have been initiatives to forge partnerships among national research institutes, international agencies and NGOs, Community Based Organisations (CBOs) and farmer groups. However, the first three agencies tend to dominate and shape the knowledge production and dissemination system. Knowledge possessed by the CBOs and farmer groups is considered less important in generating the technologies. NARC scientists are not in favour of sharing research responsibilities with other producers of knowledge. Potential arguments against devolving research responsibility to non-state actors could include such arguments as: vulnerable resources should not be privatised, there are very few competent service providers and intellectual property rights may be hijacked unduly by private business interests.

Resource poor farmers also have mixed reactions to development of new technology since NARC's research strategies and methods do not appear sensitive to their needs and constraints. For instance, the scientists tend to focus mainly on crops and less on livestock and vegetables (which are more accessible to the resource poor farmers).

When examined against the Tenth Plan's focus on poverty alleviation, NARC research seems to focus on those who have land, and a great majority of landless and land-poor farmers are excluded from the targeted group. Another bottleneck seems to be in the area of sharing or dissemination of knowledge with programme partners like the government extension agencies.

Coordination and linkages among the actors of agricultural development is important for agricultural knowledge development, its dissemination and effective use. Most of the scientists interviewed said that there was a weak coordination and knowledge partnership between NARC and the Ministry of Agriculture, which was a major constraint in developing appropriate technology. It was observed that there was an ongoing conflict and tension between NARC and the Ministry as to who had the legitimacy and power to produce knowledge. The lack of effective deliberative interface among national agricultural research centres, extension organisations and different categories of farmers and farmers' organisations was one of the constraining factors in appropriate development of knowledge systems. Research and extension organisations generally competed over the same government resources as argued by S Arunachalam (Arunachalam 2002) and, often, leaders of these institutions did not see themselves as part of a broader system.

The finding of the study show that there is lack of an effective monitoring system to identify the impact and learning from the intervention of new technologies. Though there has been more than 100 technologies generated since the establishment of NARC, there have been limited attempts to look at how these technologies are being adopted by farmers in various parts of the country, how they have been modified in various spatial and temporal contexts, and above all, what can be learnt to improve the strategy and operational techniques of research. This study indicates that many of the technologies generated by NARC are not realised fully, since most of the farmers in the study area seems to have no information on the technologies generated by NARC. Moreover, the extension agents are also unaware of the technologies generated. In many cases, the technologies generated are detached from the life of the people (culture, institutions and individual farmers). When useful, they seemed to benefit richer farmers. This finding resonates the argument made by L Yapa (Yapa 1993) that improved technology is not just a technology to feed people better by increasing food production, but it is also an instrument designed to serve the economic interest of a particular class of people.

The analysis reveals that most of the scientists at NARC are operating in the linear model of development paradigm as they think that their own knowledge is superior. They are not always ready to accept mistakes as a process of learning and refining the knowledge system. Since the research is organised primarily based on commodities and since there are limited efforts and expertise to look at cross-commodity issues to develop more generic principles of agricultural research, there is weak deliberative interface among diverse sub-systems of knowledge within the present models of research within NARC. There is a lack of feedback mechanism in helping set priorities and improving program relevance (Swanson 1997).

What is even more critical is that farmers in the study areas perceived the new varieties or seeds as a threat to the extinction of local knowledge systems. As L Yapa (Yapa 1993) holds, seeds themselves have been the material embodiment of a nexus of interacting relations between social, political and ecological aspects of society. From the personal accounts of the farmers it can be understood how the new technologies in the form of improved variety have come to be the means for domination of people and nature and how this technology can both create and destroy the knowledge system at the same time. The dominant trend of technology production by state institutions such as NARC does not seem to provide sufficient space for people to generate new ideas and become engaged in making it work. The notion of farmer as the ultimate audience of research is taken in a very generic sense, without disaggregating the class and gender, which are crucial determinants of the type of technology that could be useful. As stated by L Yapa

(Yapa 1993), the capital-intensive innovation in the package of high yielding variety soon acquires a landlord bias. As perceived by the scientists at NARC, some examples of knowledge production include development of improved variety (cereals, legumes, oilseeds etc.), disease resistant technology, seed production, animal breeding activities etc. Also, as discussed in the theoretical section of this book, scientists emphasise on technical knowledge that ignores deliberative interface with other participants and beneficiaries. Many of the NARC's knowledge systems reinforce the interests of the dominant groups.

Improving deliberative knowledge interface in agricultural technology development: A way forward

Evidence in the previous section shows that NARC is pursuing a narrow conception of knowledge – around a material product such as a new variety. NARC research themes and agendas indicate that there are limited efforts, if any, to explore agriculture and livelihood as a socio-ecological system. Interestingly, there is no framework to bridge gaps and coordinate learning between various groups of scientists. For example, no efforts are made to try out how a scientist working on research on potatoes and a scientist working on new findings on rice could communicate and learn from each other on the research possibilities and practices. Most of the knowledge acquired by the individual scientists is limited to their specific subjects of research (e.g. rice, wheat, maize, legumes, etc.). In general, the individual scientists tend to see reflection and self-monitoring as a threat since they believe in a linear model of development and consider own knowledge as superior. This is partly due to a lack of appropriate institutional policy (such as to encourage and reward analysis and sharing of innovations or mistakes for learning).

The process of knowledge generation at NARC reflects, and in turn, often reinforces the technical rationality of the scientific knowledge that is related to the material world. Little work has been done towards developing critical knowledge as most of the technology generation process at NARC to date is less sensitive to social issues such as gender, equity, culture and the stock of knowledge that the local people possess. Indeed, a major strength of research lies in taking advantage of the wisdom of the rural poor concerning the environment with which they are intimately familiar. In other words, the integration of the pro-poor approach into the overall growth process should not be expressed in terms of what the poor should receive from this process; rather, it should ask what they could offer. Indigenous intelligence, combined with enlightened training and other external assistance, may result in agricultural technologies which are manageable in scope do not rely unduly on imported technology, have low recurrent costs, and can be voluntarily maintained by farmers themselves (Jazairy *et al.* 1992).

The strategy of research needs to be segregated in two types of research: one with wider social implications with longer time frames, and the other with specific contextual domains of applications and shorter time frames. While NARC as the central research institution should continue to lead the research of the first category, local NGOs, agricultural consultants and farmer cooperatives can also take over the roles of research of the second category. The first step towards this move is to get the roles of various actors identified, spaces assessed, and roles shared on the basis of plurality of knowledge, mutual interface, and the potential to contribute to the livelihood of resource poor farmers.

In all modalities of agricultural research, farmers are the major stakeholders to utilise the agricultural technology generated. They need to be considered as the active agents of knowledge development process. Similarly, the policy and institutions of agriculture development need to be crafted in a way to promote a network of farmers – a form of civil society that promotes the knowledge system suitable for the farmers. Lessons can be learned from the emergence and development of Federation of Community Forestry Users, Nepal (FECOFUN), and a strong civil society in the field of forest resource management in Nepal (see Ojha and Timsina, this volume).

The role of NARC should not be only to develop the new technology but also to facilitate the development of new technologies in partnership with other local government and non-government actors. It should guide, facilitate, enable, monitor and promote participatory (involving farmers) and collaborative (involving NGOs and locally based agricultural consultants) technology development. In cases where partnership with local NGOs and farmers organisations have been made, the outcomes have been different, particularly in terms of bringing additional strengths in incorporating views and concerns of farmers. NARC as a national leader of agricultural research should explore and suggest ways (regulatory and fiscal measures) through which competent local organisations can be mobilised for better research and innovation.

NARC's focus on development of different technologies, with an emphasis on the yield as the indicator of success raises a key question: whether the technological focus of agricultural research is an appropriate area to focus as far as the goals of poverty alleviation is concerned. Various studies have indicated that it is entitlement or access to land-based resources that matters the most, rather than the technology per se. Lack of access to land remains an important cause of hunger and poverty. This means that for research to be more useful towards achieving poverty alleviation goal, it should not only look at the dimension of technological effectiveness but also the associated socio-economic factors that limit poor farmers' access to diverse forms of livelihood capitals, including the improved varieties.

Acknowledgement

We acknowledge the contribution of Tapendra Shah in collecting information from the field and reviewing literature.

References

Arunachalam, S. (2002). *The Global Research Village: A View from the Periphery.* A Background Paper Commissioned by the International Development Research Centre (IDRC).

Chambers, R. (1997). *Whose Reality Counts? Putting the Last First.* London: Intermediate Technology Publication.

Jazairy, I., A. Mohiuddin and P. Theresa, (eds.). (1992). *The State of World Rural Poverty: An Inquiry into its Causes and Consequences.* New York, NY: New York University Press.

JMA and APROSC (1998). *Nepal Agriculture Perspective Plan: Monitoring Report.* Kathmandu: National Planning Commission and Asian Development Bank.

NPC (2002). *The Tenth Plan* (2002–2007). Kathmandu: National Planning Commission.

NARC (2001). Annual Report, 2000/2001, Lalitpur: Nepal Agricultural Research Council.

Swanson, B. E. (1997). Strengthening Research-Extension-Farmer Linkages. In B. E. Swanson P. B. Robert, and J. S. Andrew (eds.), *Improving Agricultural Extension: A Reference Manual.* Rome: Food and Agriculture Organisation of the United Nations.

Yapa, L. (1993). What are Improved Seeds? An Epistemology of the Green Revolution, *Economic Geography,* 3: 254–273.

3

Contested Knowledge and Reconciliation in Nepal's Community Forestry: A Case of Forest Inventory Policy

Krishna P Paudel and Hemant R Ojha

Introduction

Socially powerful actors tend to influence the resource governance decisions using various forms of power. They influence the values, behaviour and action of an individual as well as institutions in various ways. In this process, how the knowledge in practice is contested and politicised in influencing such decisions is a growing concern. Increasingly, it has become more important to understand the ways through which certain knowledge is legitimised within institutions and decision making process and how it is impinging on the daily lives and struggles of the poor and powerless, especially women and indigenous people who are highly dependent on forest resources for their livelihoods. In this context, there is a need to understand better the social dynamics of natural resource management with particular reference to knowledge related politics.

Common pool resources, including forest resources, have been highly contested domains in developing countries including Nepal.

Various actors with their diverse interests are engaged and influence the overall contexts, processes and outcomes of the resource management regimes. Over the past 25 years of implementation of community forestry in Nepal, about 35 per cent of the total population is involved in the management of about 27 per cent forest land, generating 900 million rupees annually from the sale of forest products (Kanel 2004). Underpinning this development is an increased level of citizen's concern over those resources. The institution of community forestry (CF) is so strong that even in the context of the political conflict and civil war which marred the country through the 90s, greatly reducing public spheres of policy discourses, CF has become a platform for democratic exercise at local level.

In Nepal, particularly in the hills, the agriculture-based livelihood system is inseparably linked with forests ecosystems. Local forest management has been mediated by the traditional institutions, which have enabled the management of forests for generations. With the intention of learning from the local wisdom of collective action and recognising the need for promoting livelihood security and forest sustainability, CF was introduced in the late 1970s in Nepal. This involved sharing power and authority with local communities. Initially, the aim was to promote both policy and practice through building CF management processes upon existing patterns of forest resource use and social interaction in specific contexts (Malla 2002). However, in the later stages, the forms and efficiency of such institutions have been highly affected by the excessive domination of forest bureaucracy where scientific forestry knowledge has been claimed as a single, superior and authentic knowledge of forest management. A growing body of evidence shows that there exists imbalance in power relations and unequal deliberative knowledge interface while implementing CF programme, resulting in differentiated outcomes to various actors involved (Paudel 2007).

In the recent years, new CF related policies are being created without adequate public consultations. Among these, the introduction of inventory policy in community forest is one of the most debated policy issues. In this chapter, the authors demonstrate how the newly introduced inventory in CF has affected the process of planning and implementing community forestry programmes and activities at the local level. The authors demonstrate how knowledge and interest of powerful groups, mainly the government Forest Department staff and/or outside donor agencies, have dominated the process of planning and implementing community forestry programmes and activities at various levels. We also explore how local elite and powerful people sought to exercise their knowledge claim in collusion with techno-bureaucratic elites. We analyse how the dominant actors collectively as well as individually employ a range of strategies and tactics in appropriating both material as well as discursive benefits by way of enforcing their seemingly superior knowledge base.

Introduction of inventory policy in community forestry

Exclusion of primary stakeholders in planning and decision making is linked with the historical processes through which communities and forest bureaucracy evolved in Nepal. Both state services and policies are guided by the dominant techno-centric approaches of resource management where nature conservation and economic development are taken as the 'technical problems' that can be solved using technologies of scientific forestry. These old fashioned technical solution models have been introduced from earlier colonial forestry knowledge applied in India (Sivaramakrishnan 2000; Bhattarai *et al.* 2002). Despite participatory ideals and devolutionary policies, the programmes and practices of CF have been heavily affected by these models. One of the most recent cycles of contention between technocratic and civil society knowledge systems around forest management can be found around the introduction and practice of forest inventory policy instrument in Nepal. It has affected management and planning in CF.

Inventory in community forest: The problem story

In March 2000, the Ministry of Forests and Soil Conservation (MOFSC) issued a circular to District Forest Offices (DFOs) and

Community Forest User Groups (CFUGs) obliging DFOs and CFUGs to undertake detailed inventory of community forests before prescribing harvest levels of forest products in Operational Plans (OPs). According to the MOFSC, the idea was to ensure sustainable harvesting by limiting the extraction within the annual increment. Following this, the Department of Forest (DoF) issued a directive for the inventory of community forest in August 2000 along with a practical guideline for field foresters and Rangers for the assessment of growing stock and increment. It is perceived as mandatory for DFOs and Rangers to follow these directives while handing over a forest to communities or renewing existing OPs. It has created a huge debate and the policy decision has been reviewed in the light of the criticisms. A key question of the review was to explore its effects on CFUGs in relation to OPs revision and technical support and its costs. Based on the recommendations of the review team, in 2002 government issued a revised guideline and endorsed a policy provision as a continuation of the earlier guideline.

While the inventory policy intervention was actually a result of widespread concern for sustainability of community forest management, there are however, debates as regards the real impact, of these on the process and development of community forestry. Some of the positive aspects include: initiation of debates and discussions on more intensive and active management of forests, sensitisation of forest users in developing skills and knowledge on assessing forest resources reorienting rangers and foresters on the need for more in-depth and updated knowledge and skills to support community forestry, and transfer of professional knowledge to forest users through training (Ojha 2002). Indeed, it may be argued that the debate triggered by the introduction of this policy can be considered as part of improving deliberative interface between civil society and scientific knowledge systems.

However, evidence shows that despite such progressive and positive changes, several fundamental problems and issues have emerged during the implementation of the inventory policy. Since implementing this directive entailed a need for significant amount of extra efforts, knowledge, and skills on the part of forest users and rangers, the process of hand over of many new community forests is delayed or even halted (Ojha 2002). A study by N Dhital *et al.* (Dhital 2003) shows that there are only a couple of forest rangers in a district who can skillfully provide technical support needed to conduct the inventory. This has delayed in forest handover. Similarly, the renewal of expiring operational plans has also been delayed because of the lack of human resources to support, which implies a suspension of CFUG use rights and management interventions. In many cases, since the government has not made provisions for alternative ways of delivering services to forest users in this regard (such as through private and NGO sector), the communities have been forced to pay rents or charges for speedy resolution. All these have weakened the hard earned trust between the government and communities, leading ultimately to far-reaching consequences both in terms of sustainable forest management and community livelihood (Ojha 2002).

Arguably, Department of Forest has an interest in community forest inventories for two purposes. First, the department's perspective of ensuring technical requirements of scientific forestry in the name of management. This action seemed reasonable as forest staff are the responsible authorities and are liable to ensure that CFUG operational plans are within the sustainable capacity of the forest. However, this has been manipulated for the reason of legitimising their control, rather than pursuing a genuine cause of ensuring forest sustainability. Forestry staff with close connection to the powerful elite were found to be involved in manipulating the levels of forest harvest prescriptions to maximise their own interests (Dhital *et al.* 2003). Second, forest staff can use inventory to control the actual processes of forestry operations. Formally, the forestry staff are authorised to check whether operational plans, including the code of forest harvesting, have been properly implemented or not. It is obvious that these provisions serve the interests of the forest bureaucracy to control users in relation to both resource use planning and implementation. For example, many field experiences show that the complex tables included in the CFUG operational plans after the introduction of forest inventory guideline, practically compelled CFUGs to call rangers in most of their executive committee meetings to take decisions relating to forest management and harvesting. This technical aspect of the inventory in many situations has further disadvantaged the illiterate, who are generally the poor, in their effort to negotiate forest management arrangements as informed users/decision-makers.

The issue of forest inventory in practice

N Dhital et *al.* (Dhital 2003) identified that the prescribed form of forest inventory in CF is very costly for the forestry users to accomplish. They reported that a qualified Ranger with at least four additional supporters (either Forest Guards or CFUG members), require 12 to 15 working days to carryout an inventory in an area of 50 hectares at the intensity specified in the inventory guideline in average forest conditions[4]. If the Rangers and local assistants are paid at the normal rate of daily allowances (which is at the rate of NRs.[5] 300 per working day and NRs. 125 for assistants), the estimated cost of an inventory of 50 hectare community forest with an average condition at the recommended intensity is NRs. 10,800 to 13,500 (to cover stationary, equipment, social survey, plan writing, analysis and documentation, and contingency costs are not included). This shows that a huge amount of resource is needed to carry out the CF inventory which is beyond the current level of funding available to DFOs and financial position of most CFUGs. At the same time, it raises even more basic questions as to whether we need to go for such a detailed and scientific forest inventory in community forests and who benefits from the inventory as such.

In relation to technical human resource, there is always a deficit of technically competent human resource capable of providing the required

---

[4]   Average condition of forest has been considered in this study as a forest area with 40–70 per cent crown coverage and 20–25^0 slopes

[5]   USD 1 = NRs. 70

services envisaged by the CF inventory. For example, in the hill districts of Nepal, on an average, there are only 10 Rangers in each district who are capable of carrying out inventory (Dhital *et al.* 2003). However, there are some Forest Guards as well as other local facilitators who are capable of carrying out inventory works, but their capability has not been recognised. Similarly, after the introduction of inventory as mandatory task in CF, the working days for preparing OP in CF have increased by three-fold. For example, a forest ranger in far-western hill district of Dadeldhura used to spend seven working days to facilitate a CFUG in preparing an OP for a forest of 50 hectares. However, now the ranger needs at least 21 working days to do the same job with inventory (Dhital *et al.* 2003). Many other Rangers consulted also shared similar experiences.

Many of the community forest users have expressed that the guideline is not only hard to understand but it is also rigid, complex, time-consuming and costly. They mentioned that CFUGs are insufficiently involved in the process. At the same time, they believe that it is in the interest of forestry professionals to make it complex to oblige forest users to consult foresters while preparing OPs and inventories. Ideally, the inventory results should be presented in formats that users can understand, and then the users should prepare the plan in consultation with Rangers, who should play the role of explaining and interpreting the analysis of inventory data and helping the users to prepare the plan. However, users are skeptical to say that the inventory has created the situation to write their operational plans by Rangers as they do not know how to interpret the inventory data in their OP, which ultimately disempowers the forest users, who are the mangers of the forest resources at local levels.

In the context of poor security situation over the past 10 years, only local Forest Guards and Community Based Organisations (CBOs) have been able to undertake fieldwork such as inventory. However, most DFOs and their staff are reluctant to accept services provided from outside the DFO. DFO, Banke (in western Terai of Nepal) suggested that there should be either a temporary hiring system of Rangers by DFO, or payments should be channelled through DFO to other service providers. Otherwise, in his opinion, it would be very difficult to recognise the adequacy of their work. DFO, Baglung in the central middle hills suggests enlarging the organisational structure thereby deputing more Rangers and officers to the field. It was mentioned that services provided by outsiders would be approved given that it is adequately monitored by DFO offices (Dhital *et al.* 2003). A common concern raised by DFO staff was that service providers must be accountable for their work. They pointed out the need for a nationally accepted standard or legal framework for the accountability of service providers. Accountability could be ensured by carefully drawing up contracts that include sanctions and definitions for inadequate performance, as well as mechanisms for checking the quality of the work by DFO staff.

In summary, the evidence from the study suggests that a major source of the inventory problem is a result of the government forestry department being the sole service provider, which, due to limited technical capacity and responsiveness to users, and in some cases, rent seeking behaviour, has not been able to meet the escalating demand for inventory related services. This is compounded by a concurrent lack of alternative service providers, due to the limited recognition given to the private service providers in the forestry service.

A detailed study carried out in 28 hill districts by N Dhital *et al.* (Dhital 2003) has identified that a total of 7,048 CFs are handed over but only 21.53 per cent of these (1,518) have been inventoried. The problem persists with further expansion of the number of CFUGs. But in the 10 districts studied, less than 10 CFs have been inventoried. They have identified various reasons behind such backlogs: unresponsiveness and unaccountable DFO practices, negligence or lack of technical competency on the part of government forestry staff, and the absence of alternative service providers. As a result, there is a significant delay in forest handover and renewal of OPs.

With the introduction of the inventory in CF, various underlying intentions and behaviour of the forestry professionals have surfaced. For example, many of the forestry officials disagree with the provision of Annual Allowable Cut (AAC) in inventory guideline. They believe that the Current Annual Increment (CAI) is far below the AAC mentioned in the earlier community forestry guideline. Their argument is that these recommendations would allow room for over-harvesting. At the same time, consideration for variables like grazing, fire, encroachment, illegal felling, girdling and landslides should be quantified and deducted from AACs to maintain the fragile ecosystem of the Siwaliks and the mountains. These arguments are reasonably valid from the technical perspective of inventory. However, it seems that DFOs are looking for more discretionary rights in the guideline regarding the extent of products to be harvested from CFs.

The problem around the inventory is essentially a tension around the power relations of the actors involved. The increased influence of technical knowledge through forestry inventory has triggered a shift of the power from ordinary forestry users to forestry professionals as the latter have control over the technical aspects of the forest inventory. Many of the forestry professionals are reluctant to discuss the change in the power structure after the inventory intervention. They would rather continue to interpret the policy as technically inevitable and important for ensuring sustainable forest management. But in fact, as discussed earlier, the power has shifted from CFUGs to DFOs as a result of the inventory policy instrument, as most CFUG decisions regarding forest product use and forest development activities can only be made with the consultation and consent of DFO staff.

Forest users know when their OP expires and that it must be renewed to further manage the forest and use forest products. However, due to lack of needed technical support in undertaking forest inventory and revising the OPs, they have in many cases not been able to renew the OPs and continue the forestry operations smoothly. In addition, the level of awareness amongst forest users about community forestry is much lower in many cases compared to what is hoped or assumed at the centre, resulting in forest management decisions being made by the Ranger in many cases. This has created an environment whereby users ignore the inventory and OP renewal and continue to harvest forest products in an unplanned and informal manner. This situation challenges the assumptions regarding the need of an OP and the whole idea of planned forest management for sustainability and equity. Local communities involved in community forestry are yet to perceive the inventory as a management tool; they see it as a bureaucratic requirement. This reflects the scenario of changing power structures in community forestry following the enactment of inventory forest policy.

The above mentioned facts and figures are evident of negative consequences of the policy measure primarily due to the creation of unequal deliberative knowledge interface, particularly between the forest administration and CFUGs. The technocratic imposition made by many foresters, including the monopolistic application of forestry knowledge while carrying inventory have further disadvantaged the illiterate, who are generally poor, in their effort to negotiate forest management arrangements as informed user/decision-makers. This situation challenges the assumptions regarding the need of an OP and undermines the whole idea of planned forest management for sustainability and equity. Most of the foresters who believe in the application of scientific traditional forestry as an approach to managing community forests see this intervention as an opportunity for them to actually apply the scientific tenets of forestry.

Inventory in community forestry: An issue of knowledge politics

Demand and supply relations of the forest products in CFUG are issues more socio-political in naure rather than technical. While determining the level of precision, one needs to consider what level of precision is actually needed to formulate demand and supply relations of the forest products available for sustainable harvesting and what would be the cost and benefit in sum. As argued earlier:

> The level of precision needed in knowing the direction and speed of a landing plane is not same for a CFUG trying to estimate how much fuel wood it should expect next year from the community forest. Forest users would not be prepared to invest a tremendous amount of effort to elevate the precision of firewood estimation from quintal to kilogram. Also, it is important to know how essential it is for them to know beforehand such a detailed strategy. They would rather prefer to distribute among themselves whatever amount would accrue at the time of harvesting, using spatial control approach to sustainable harvesting, and the time thus saved would be used in farming or earning wages (Ojha 2002).

This does not mean a denial of science in forest management, but certainly raises a question as to which approach to science should be taken while suggesting the standards and procedures of resource analysis to forest users and why.

Similarly, the current focus of the inventory is on assessing the stock and increment of timber products, and there are limited techniques recommended to assess a wide range of non-timber forest products that are available in community forests. Most of the inventory data are quantitative, and the rich qualitative insights available in the local communities are not collected as part of developing the plans for forest management. A mechanistic and quantitative technique suggested in the guideline does not allow villagers' common sense to get incorporated into the analysis process (Ojha 2002). This creates limited understanding and ownership on the part of forest users, even though there is a huge supply of external scientific services. A CFUG secretary in Dolakha district informed (Ojha 2002) that after finishing the field inventory and calculation by a Forest Ranger, none of the local members could believe the figure of Chiraito stock that was estimated by the Ranger. In this situation, neither the Ranger's technique of inventory can persuade the users how the estimation came, nor the latter challenge

Ranger's analytical scheme. The result is that there is a scientific inventory, with limited insights and uses to local people (Ojha 2002).

No doubt, with the expansion of community forestry, there has been a growing concern for sustainability of forest resource in community forests. As discussed earlier, the inventory requirement was initially proposed as a measure for ensuring harvesting level. This came particularly within the Department of Forests and forestry professional circles, in view of a few extreme cases in which excessive harvesting was reported from community forests (Ojha 2002). As Ojha argued, it came at the time when struggles between the advocates of people-oriented forestry and those who wanted to retain technocratic role of government foresters was in the peak among the actors involved in the forestry sector including donor funded forestry projects. At the same time, because of the national political environment, the more anti-community forestry bureaucrats in power, this was further reinforced by many old-fashioned technocrats with a fear of losing their role in decentralised forestry including community forestry. All these conditions together led to a favourable situation for those technocrats who wished to respond to sustainability issues using their technocratic knowledge base.

One can argue that the government officials have always been worried on the possible over-harvesting, which according to their assumption, is due to the lack of technical management. Thus, from this perspective, inventory on CF was a technical instrument for the assessment of its resource base, which was technically important and essential too. However, if this was the case, the issue is not why they wished to invite CFUG and other actors while formulating such policy instruments in a wider process of participation. Very often, it is said that denial of local participation by technocrats is justified on the ground that local users lack technical knowledge, although there have been substantial evidence of rich ecological knowledge and indigenous management practices among forest users. Several other actors outside the government, who could have contributed to the process of devising more accessible inventory policy, were also denied any participation. The result was that the Department of Forest took a short-cut technocratic approach without creating spaces for deliberations to create knowledge interface. They rather sought to transfer formal technical knowledge of forest bureaucrats, without adequately linking technical and institutional insights for effective management of forest.

The claim of forest bureaucracy as regards having technical knowledge on forestry is losing its foundation. One of the reasons for this is that there are very few cases in the 50 year's history of forest bureaucracy in Nepal, where government foresters have got opportunities to apply and manipulate their knowledge systems. Except one plantation forestry project in Sagarnath in east-central Terai, there are no significantly viable cases of government-initiated forestry practices in natural forest. At worst, many forest technicians and officials who have professional degrees of forest management from national and Western Universities are hardly in a position to offer the kind of technical advice that forest users demand for. Most of forest technocrats' time is spent on judicial, administrative and managerial jobs, with little chance of practicing a specialist job of forestry. Our criticism of old-fashioned forestry is based on the notion of habitus (as outlined in the introduction chapter), which means that the attributes demonstrated by the individual forestry officials are not solely the properties of the conscious domain of their agency, but actually effected through culturally deep-seated practices and historically framed social structures. The implication is that there has to be a debate on these deep seated foundations of technocratic habitus, going beyond documenting what individual foresters do.

In some situations, such deep seated foundations of knowledge are brought to the process of critical scrutiny. There has recently been a significant force of foresters who have attempted to maintain their technical expertise and would like to offer technical services to complement local knowledge. But working environment is such that these types of professionals are disempowered, and are positioned in such areas where they get frustrated and hence, are leaving the jobs.

There are some who have knowledge and commitment and are trying to bridge the local and scientific knowledge that professionals and villagers hold, through informal strategic alliances across government, NGOs and communities.

The issue of sustainable harvesting is not limited to technical knowledge, but is influenced more by institutional and political factors within which both CFUG and forest technicians operate. The very foundation of this intervention does not clearly articulate with the prevailing institutional and political contexts, and despite good intentions, this has been resulting in unintended consequences and negative effects over CF Management (Ojha 2002). This implies that government should look at its own service providing capacity before embarking on any policy intervention.

The lack of committed people within and outside the government and community organisations, and competent and politically committed service providing agencies and individuals, who could challenge the power of both government officials and the local power elites further exacerbate the situation. In some cases these type of interventions by which local power elites will be trained, legitimises their power and authority together with the additional power of 'formal knowledge' as human capital. In most cases, they have monopolised power and knowledge. Not all concerned benefit equally, and neither is the cost so distributed. Although science could be neutral, the application of it cannot be so, nor can its outcomes be so, as discussed in earlier sections. It is however not to say that all local power elites are bad. There are numerous examples that 'good leadership' has contributed to positive outcomes at resource and livelihood level.

The situation is that the inventory policy has legitimised a knowledge system that is not owned by or accessible to large number of users, who are supposed to participate in forest management decisions as well-informed resource managers. This has put many users in difficult positions in terms of participation in the decision-making as informed resource managers. This means that mandating extra technicality in the

CFUG system involves cost in terms of participation, particularly of those who are illiterate, poor and disadvantaged (Ojha 2002). If this is the result, then the policy instrument may go counter to the community forestry goal of equitable livelihoods.

Another issue is related to the understanding of sustainability, which is taken in the narrow technical sense. The current policy instrument specifies the technical arrangements of resource use, which essentially interferes with users' independent decision on the harvesting levels (Ojha 2002). Political scientists regard this as a process of limiting 'constitutive choice' of CFUGs (Varughese and Ostrom 2001), which will lead to limited motivation and enthusiasm on sustainable forest management. In other words, if a CFUG feels bad or gets discouraged through a technically sound guideline, the institutional base of sustainable forest management is ruined, and the outcomes may sometimes be counter-productive (Ojha 2002). It is essential that sustainable forest management should be understood in terms of the interactions of social, economic, political and ecological systems rather narrowly defined technical term.

The scientific forest inventory and gap in deliberative interface

As we discussed in the earlier section, the scientific element that underpins the principle and practice of forest inventory has led to the practice of collecting excessive data in the field, spending a lot of time and resources in calculating costs and benefits leading to a significant delay in decisions and actions. More importantly, the science of inventory is understood in a narrow sense of analysing resource attributes isolating inextricably linked human perceptions, knowledge and actions (Ojha 2002). This means that an emphasis is put on assessing resource situation from outsider's perspective, ignoring the way local people understand and respond to the ecological issues. Dut to the approach of technocratic science which is based on sophisticated tools and techniques and emphasised in inventory, we are unable to make use of the vast amount of knowledge that has emerged and sustained through local knowledge system over which local users would have better control.

Overemphasis on quick fix technical approach ignores the strengths of adaptive approaches to resource management that encourages learning by applying principles even in complex situations. In the recent advances on adaptive management, there are more conscious ways to maximise learning through integrating monitoring systems with action plans, thus making it possible to move under conditions of uncertainty (Lee 1993). In the process, efforts may be made to promote deliberative interface among diverse knowledge systems for making decisions and organising actions. The current inventory science involves using a huge amount of efforts at the beginning, while allowing limited opportunities for deliberation and learning during the process.

The current inventory approach necessitates several supportive quantitative research data such as biomass tables, growth rate, and several others, which are hardly available for all important species in many different bio-physical contexts. This lack of supportive information base is a critically limiting factor of the current approach to resource assessment.

In summary, the externally imposed, detail-oriented, quantitative science that is behind the inventory is neither useful nor desirable for community forest management, and it only serves the hidden political interests of powerful bureaucratic and professional elites. Introduction of this type of inventory obligation to CFUGs widens the power gap that already exists between the forest bureaucrats and users. Since the inventory has been set as a pre-condition for forest handover, and that the service is delivered only through the government staff who are limited in number to provide services, many CFUGs/communities are desperately waiting for service. This compels CFUG to be loyal to and comply with any conditions set by the staff, if they want to go for CF process envisioned.

Similarly, the policy framework of inventory fails to work out strategies of delivering services needed to implement the more rigorous procedure of resource assessment. While the guideline specified the kind of procedure to be followed for an inventory, it was not put clearly in the context of existing capacities of DoF, thus ignoring the need to set out policies that would address the service supply side. While it was clear that this would require tremendous amount of technical support, which is beyond the prevailing supply capacity of DoF, there was no policy to encourage service delivery from the NGO or private sector. This left DoF as the monopolist in the delivery of technical services, which not only limited choices to people for competitive services, but also led to non-availability of services and reinforcement of bureaucratic power discouraging and patronising forest user groups who are legally independent of DFO (Ojha 2002). As discussed earlier, complying with this requirement involves a huge amount of efforts on the part of CFUGs as well as the service provider. In many cases, since there is no adequate budget at DoF, rangers have openly sought 'consultancy fee' from CFUGs, which is often many times higher than what CFUG can afford.

The monopoly of power, knowledge and service provisioning with forest bureaucracy has created conditions for exploitation of people through rent seeking. Although there are evidence of some educated community members learning to practice this external scientific technique through training, this does not mean that larger public has gained a capacity to get engaged in informed participation in the forest management debate. This will elevate a few community elites to a position in which forestry professionals can work and communicate with, but this raises a question of participation of all the poor and marginalised members of the community (Malla 2002; Ojha 2002; Timsina 2002). At the same time, this can undermine the potential of local knowledge in managing local resources. As we discussed earlier, the current science of inventory undermines the very essence of inclusion, participation and democratic exercise, which should go hand in hand towards promoting livelihood security and forest sustainability within CFUG. However, the perceptions of both forest officials and the CFUG members reinforce that there exist a patron client relationship between the two (Malla 2001). At the same time, the DoF and its field staff, mainly Rangers and Forest Guards, fail to provide relevant and adequate technical services to farmers, partly because of the inherent limitations of bureaucracy to reach people and partly because of the limited skills and competencies to deal with the emerging complexities of community forestry (Springate-Baginski *et al.* 2003).

Conclusion

Forest governance is primarily an interface between two key knowledge systems: knowledge of local forest users and knowledge of forest officials. The chapter has analysed how these knowledge systems contradict and what scope exists for improving the deliberative interface. It has been demonstrated that forest inventory policy instrument enforced in the practice of community forestry indicates domination of technocratic knowledge systems of forestry experts.

The inventory policy instrument in CF has resulted in a range of problems for different stakeholders while attempting to implement it. The evidence from the study suggests that a major source of the problem is related to monopolising the delivery of inventory related services by the government forest department, which due to limited technical capacity and responsiveness to users, and in some cases, rent seeking behaviour, has not been able to meet the escalating demand for inventory related services. There is a lack of alternative service providers, due to the limited recognition of the non-governmental service providers in the forestry business. Capacity building of locally based NGOs/CBOs who can provide the services requires special consideration.

The technocratic knowledge intervention in the form of inventory in CF has reinforced the alliance of two sets of power elites – professional elite from forest bureaucracy and the local elite from community organisations. This has led to weakened institutional base for sustainable forest management, as well as reduction of opportunities for livelihood of the poor and marginalised groups of people in the community. Since imposing a policy instrument on forest inventory in community forestry is a highly political issue, implying a potential change in power, positions and interests of stakeholders involved, a deliberative approach of change would be required. This would mean that all concerned, including the representatives of the communities, engage in a process of effective communication, negotiation, collaboration, and even conflicts so that they are able to arrive at negotiated visions, strategies and policy instruments that better address the issues and opportunities (Ojha 2007). The debate should take place on all aspects of the issue – technical, political, institutional, service delivery, and economic.

Use of inventory in CF should be recognised as a tool primarily for the users to have appropriate information on which to base their management decisions. The people responsible for most of the inventory work should be the users themselves. For this, appropriate training and guidelines with a series of options for different local forest situations should be developed. Instead of imposing a centrally designed inventory guideline, outsiders should assist users to design appropriate inventory, and analyse and interpret the resulting data.

References

Bhattarai, K. D. Conway and N. R. Shrestha (2002). The Vacillating Evolution of Forestry Policy in Nepal: Historically Manipulated, Internally Mismanaged. *International Development Planning Review,* 34 (3): 315–338.

Dhital, N. and K. P. Paudel and H. Ohja (2003). Inventory of Community Forests in Nepal: Problems and Opportunities. *Journal of Forest and Livelihood,* 3 (1): 62–66.

Kanel, K. (2004). Issues and Challenges of Community Forestry in Nepal. In K. R. Kanel, P. Mathema, B. R. Kandel, D. R. Niraula, A. R. Sharma and M. Gautam (eds.), *Proceedings of Fourth National Workshop on Community Forestry.* Kathmandu: Department of Forest.

Lee, K. N. (1993). *Compass and Gyroscope: Integrating Science and Politics for the Environment.* Washington DC: Island Press.

Malla, Y. M., A. Lawrence, R. Barnes, K. P. Paudel, H. R. Ojha and K. Green (2002). *Common Property Forest Management in Nepal: Developing Monitoring Systems for Use at the Local Level.* Research Report. Reading and Kathmandu: The University of Reading and Forest Action.

Malla, Y. B. (2001). Changing Policies and the Persistence of Patron-Client Relations in Nepal: Stakeholders' Responses to Changes in Forest Policies. *Environmental History,* 6 (2): 287–307.

Ojha H. R. (2002). *A Critical Assessment of Scientific and Political Dimensions of the Issue of Community Forests Inventory in Nepal.* A Policy Discussion Note. Kathmandu: ForestAction, Nepal

Ojha, H. R. (2007). *Engaging Bourdieu and Habermas to Reframe Governance Debate in Nepalese Terai.* Unpublished PhD Thesis. Norwich, UK: School of Development Studies at the University of East Anglia.

Paudel K. P. (2007). Knowledge, Power and Practice in Community Forestry: A Case from Nepal's Terai. *PhD Thesis.* UK: The University of Reading.

Paudel, K. P. and H. R. Ojha (2007). From Imposed Indicators to Co-Creating Meanings in Nepal. In I. Guijt (ed.) *Negotiated Learning: Collaborative Monitoring in Resource Management.* Washington D C: Resources for the Future.

Sivaramakrishnan, K. (2000). State Science and Development Histories: Encoding Local Forestry Knowledge in Bangal. *Development and Change,* 31: 61–89.

Springate-Baginski, O., N. Yadav, O.P. Dev and J. Soussan (2003). Institutional Development of Forest User Groups in Nepal: Processes and Indicators. *Journal of Forest and Livelihood,* 3 (1):21–36.

Timsina, N. P. (2002). Political Economy of Forest Resource Use and Management: An Analysis of Stakeholders' Interests and Actions in Nepal's Community Forest Management. *PhD Thesis.* UK: The University of Reading.

Varughese, G. and E. Ostrom (2001). The Contested Role of Heterogeneity in Collective Action: Some Evidence from Community Forestry in Nepal. *World Development,* 29 (5): 747–765.

4

From Grassroots to Policy Deliberation: The Case of Community Forest Users' Federation in Nepal

Hemant R Ojha and Netra P Timsina

Introduction

This chapter discusses the emergence of the Federation of Community Forestry Users, Nepal (FECOFUN) and its contribution to the process of participatory and deliberative governance in the forestry sector of Nepal. In particular, this chapter discusses how the forest dependent civil society groups were able to enhance their deliberative interface with various groups of actors engaged in the field of forestry, mainly: techno-bureaucrats, formal political agents (mainly political parties) and development agencies. The purpose is to explicate conditions and processes that enable or constrain the ability of local forest-dependent citizens to participate in the policy and practice of forest governance.

Despite repeated pleas for the participatory and deliberative governance of environmental resources (Fischer 1999; Dryzek 2000; Fischer 2000; Smith 2003; Ojha 2006; Parkins and Mitchell 2005), there is still a predominance of technocratic values and institutions in environmental decision-making (Backstrand 2004; Pokharel and

Ojha 2005). This is especially true in the context of forest management in the Global South where centralised and technically-oriented colonial approaches of the past continue to dominate the day to day practices of forest management, policies and their implementation (Peluso 1992; Shivaramakrishnan 2000; Sundar 2000, 2001; Roth 2004; Sarin 2005). The rhetoric of decentralisation and devolution of forest management have often been couched in an agenda of extending bureaucratic control rather than advancing the genuine empowerment of the local people (Shrestha 1999; Sarin *et al.* 2003; Shrestha 2001).

The history of forest governance in Nepal is dominated by the strategic interests of forest technocrats and other state actors, and there has been limited room for civil society to participate in the formulation of policies. While the feudal rulers of the country appropriated forest lands and trees for their benefit (Regmi 1977), the advent of modernisation project in Nepal in the name of development contributed to the expansion of the technocratic state (Blaikie *et al.* 2001). The colonial schooling and orientation of the forestry profession and its subsequent transplant in the bureaucracy means that there was little appreciation of democratic deliberation with people in forestry matters.

The twin crises of environment and poverty in the late 1980's have led to the evolution of participatory forestry practices (Hobley 1996; Malla 1997), creating significant spaces for local forest dependent communities to participate in the governance and management of forest resources. Following the transfer of forest management rights to Community Forest User Groups (CFUGs) throughout the country since the late eighties, citizens have become organised at different levels to voice their concerns in forest policy making. A remarkable initiative in this regard is the emergence and development of FECOFUN as a nation-wide federation of over 11000 CFUGs across the country (covering about one-third of the country's population), out of the total of 14000 CFUGs. FECOFUN has had significant impact on the policies and practices of natural resource governance and development in Nepal. In a span of just over 10 years, it has established itself as the nation's largest civil society organisation with branches established in 74 of the 75 districts in the country.

The term governance has different meanings, but a common understanding is that it refers to how a social group is formed and how its rules are constituted and enforced. We take a deliberative perspective of governance following theories of deliberative democracy (Chambers 1996; Forester 1999; Fisher 2003 and Young 2003). From this perspective, we contend that any use of coercion and power (such as group rules and constitution) is democratically legitimate when it is constituted through reasoned debate among concerned citizens. In deliberative democracy, political leaders or bureaucrats do not make decisions on their own; rather they seek opinions from concerned groups of citizens through public processes. Such public deliberation has an intrinsic value of enhancing civic virtue and public culture. When public decisions are made in this way, not only is the quality of decisions in terms of justice likely to be enhanced, but also the decisions can be considered democratically legitimate and morally binding among the citizens. The legitimacy of any use of restraint (such as 'rules' or 'penalties') is only justified when the citizens choose it freely. Deliberation is thus a fundamental process of civic engagement in governance and social change.

Framing the analysis of FECOFUN from deliberative governance perspective adds to the understanding of how and when citizens can and can not get organised, collectively learn and influence state policies and governance. It will also demonstrate an innovative way through which the state and civil society are able to enter into a process of deliberative knowledge interface and social learning. The paper specifically addresses the ways through which FECOFUN has resisted the technocratic domination of the state in forest related decisions and practices, and brought alternative perspectives that allow more inclusive and equitable governance of the resources.

This chapter is based on the authors' direct engagement with community forestry and FECOFUN related processes over the past 10 years. While working for various agencies in Nepal, including

ForestAction Nepal, there were opportunities to participate in the events and processes of FECOFUN. In addition, the chapter provides an updated analysis of two earlier studies on FECOFUN which were independently conducted (Timsina 2003 and Ojha 2002).

Emergence and expansion of forest users' federation

Evolution

The democratic political changes in Nepal beginning in 1990 have allowed for the rapid growth of civil society activities. FECOFUN emerged in this period. It is a network of CFUGs, which are local level institutions for forest management under Nepal's Community Forestry policy. CFUGs are registered with District Forest Offices (DFOs) as perpetually self-governed bodies according to the Forest Act 1993 and the Forest Regulation 1995 (GON/MFSC 1995). They are legally recognised as self-governed local organisations for the management, conservation and utilisation of communal forests in Nepal. Villagers who depend on forests for their livelihood are organised into a CFUG and are entitled to manage and utilise part(s) of accessible national forests as community forests, as per their operational plan (OP) approved by the DFO.

Since the inception of user group based community forestry in the early 1990s, there has been a rapid expansion of CFUGs throughout the country, particularly in the middle hills (Kanel and Kandel 2004). With the increase in number of CFUGs to a few hundreds in the early nineties, ideas of CFUGs networking emerged within CFUG leaders, project staff, and DFOs. Localised informal networks of CFUGs then came into existence initially in Dhankuta and Bhojpur districts in the east of Nepal. These preliminary networking experiences were self-initiated in the beginning but later supported by bilateral forestry projects[6]. The intention of these efforts was to create forums for learning

---

[6] Key projects which supported include Nepal-UK Community Forestry Project funded by DFID, Nepal Australia Community Forestry Project, both of which lasted for over a decade in various forms.

and sharing among CFUGs. The supporting projects responded to such local initiatives positively as networking mechanisms were considered as a potential means for providing post-formation services to CFUGs and for effective program planning. Such local level networking experiences were followed by initiatives in the form of national level CFUG networking meetings. With support from donor forestry projects, several discussions and gatherings of CFUG representatives were held between 1993 and 1995, including a national workshop of CFUGs in which 40 CFUGs from 28 districts participated. These events provided representatives of CFUGs from around the country an opportunity to identify ways and means to promote and advocate the community forestry agenda and users' rights over forest management, and to explore the need for a users' national level institution to work proactively in this line. Later, these initiatives were merged and FECOFUN was formed in 1995. Table 4.1 outlines key milestones and events in the evolution of FECOFUN.

Shrestha *et al.* (Shrestha *et al.* 1997) have identified four types or stages of CFUG networking and federation building in Nepal. These stages are briefly outlined with some modifications by the authors to incorporate additional observations. The *first stage* was locally initiated informal networks that were small and confined to CFUGs located close to one another. The *second stage* came when projects and DFOs started to use these networks for planning and information extraction. The *third stage* of network development emerged when CFUGs started to cluster around specific themes or issues (e.g. networks of CFUGs on resin in Dhankuta). Finally, *the stage of federation building* started with the formation of an ad-hoc committee, which then extended membership and facilitated the formation of district chapters.

As the constitution of FECOFUN stipulates, the main objective of this network is to promote cooperation and collaboration among member forest user groups and enhance learning from the sharing of experiences. It also aims to raise the awareness of the forest users about their rights of access to, and responsibilities towards the management

Table 4.1 Key events and milestones in the evolution of FECOFUN

- On July 2, 1992, representatives of Sildhunga, Patle Pangsing, Pancha Kanya and Sansari-Suke Pokhari community forestry user groups in Dhankuta Municipality eastern hills of Nepal had raised their curiosity with the staff of DFO and Koshi Hill Community Forestry Project (a bilateral undertaking of Nepal Government and the UK government) about the number of community forestry groups, and their working approach and how they could best share experiences between the community forestry user groups. In response, the project staff, DFO staff and users themselves decided to hold a workshop and formed a nine-member organising committee.
- On July 24–26, 1992, the committee organised a workshop of forest user groups with two representatives from each of the CFUGs within Dhankuta district.
- Learning from this networking workshop, several other networking meetings were organised in the district and later DFO also included networking as one of the activities of their annual programme.
- Similar networking workshops were organised in Bhojpur and other districts in the Koshi Hills.
- The networking processes rapidly spread from Koshi Hills to other areas of the country.
- In February 1993 the first national workshop of community forest user groups was organised in Dhankuta district. 41 representatives from 40 forest user groups of 28 districts participated the workshop. Networking was seen as a means to solve problems and to fulfill the needs of users.
- On 23–26 February 1993, the second national community forestry workshop was organised and the conclusions and lessons from the workshop of forest user groups in Dhankuta were presented in the workshop. This workshop became a milestone in the movement for CFUGs networking throughout the country.
- In May 1995, an NGO called WATCH organised a workshop of community forestry and private forestry plantation user groups at Budol, in Kavre district (near Kathmandu). This workshop elected a 13 member ad hoc committee for the Federation of Community Forest Users, Nepal.
- In June 1995, an ad-hoc FECOFUN committee was formed in a gathering of CFUG representatives from 35 districts and NGOs. This workshop decided to establish a contact office in Kathmandu and formed a committee to prepare a draft constitution for FECOFUN.
- In September 1995, the federation was registered in Kathmandu District Administration Office and became a legally recognised entity.
- The first general assembly was held in March 1996 with representatives from 38 districts. The general assembly elected a 27 member national executive committee.
- In the third year (in 1998) after the emergence of FECOFUN, there were efforts by some groups to split FECOFUN or create parallel federations, but these were not successful.

Source: H R Ojha, 2002

of the country's forest resources as outlined in the government forest policy documents. The other objective is to take on a lobbying and advocacy role on behalf of the forest users and to ensure that the community forestry policy objectives are accomplished.

Currently, FECOFUN has a eight-tiered structure including (FECOFUN 2006):

a. *General Assembly* (the supreme body of FECOFUN consisting of equal number of men and women representatives from all the districts)

b. *National Council* (second main body of the FECOFUN comprising one male and one female representative from each district and office bearers of the National Executive Committee)

c. *National Executive Committee* (the main executive body comprising one male and one female representative from each of the 14 zones[7])

d. *Steering Committee* (the regular working committee comprising Chairperson, Vice-chair person, Member-secretary plus three members selected by the National Executive Committee)

e. *Regional Coordination Committee*

f. *District Branch Committee*

g. *Range Post Level Committee*

h. *Village FECOFUN.* FECOFUN's constitution requires that 50 per cent of all the positions at all levels be given to women. The office tenure of the National Executive Committee is four years. The tenure of district chapters is three years and is elected by district-level assembly. The second highest body of FECOFUN is the national council which meets every one and a half years.

FECOFUN central office is registered with the District Administration Office (DAO) and its constitution has provisions to

---

7   A zone is a politico-geographic division of the country consisting of a group of districts. There are a total of 14 zones in Nepal.

establish district chapters throughout the country. The district chapters are therefore an extension of FECOFUN, registered as per the NGOs Registration Act 1976 and they need not be registered separately in the districts. This Act regulates most of the NGOs in Nepal. While the CFUGs are required to work in close coordination with DFOs, FECOFUN is entirely independent of the government except the registration and renewal related obligations that it has to meet under the Act. According to the constitution of FECOFUN, district chapters can only be formed when there are at least 10 CFUGs that have been registered at FECOFUN as members. Any CFUG with a registered constitution can become a member of FECOFUN. At the time of affiliation to FECOFUN, a CFUG has to pay a membership fee of NRs.[8] 235, and NRs. 100 annually for renewal of membership. The fees paid by CFUGs are divided among the various committees as follows: 40 per cent to central FECOFUN, 20 per cent each to District and Range Post chapters, and 10 per cent to village FECOFUN.

Central FECOFUN has a secretariat consisting of seven full time committee members and over a dozen full time technical and logistic support staff. There are six different units headed by a coordinator: legal advocacy, organisational strengthening, Non-Timber Forest Products and Income Generation, Women empowerment, Resource Centre (FECOFUN 2002), and policy advocacy campaign. These units coordinate and organise activities at central, regional and local levels in collaboration with a number of donor and technical support organisations. An advisory board consisting of NGO activists and forestry project staff provides constant guidance and inputs to the FECOFUN central secretariat.

The size of FECOFUN and its scale of activities are also indicated by the amount of financial resources mobilised annually. In the fiscal year 2002–2003, for instance, it spent NRs. 15.7 millions (around USD 2,10,000) on administration and programmes (FECOFUN 2003). Of this amount, only 5.19 per cent came from FECOFUN's internal

---

[8] 1 USD = NRs. 70

sources, such as membership fees, renewal fees, interests from the bank, advertisements, services and publication sales, while the rest was raised through partner organisations and donor grants. Although this indicates a great donor interest in supporting FECOFUN, raising internal contributions to make FECOFUN financially more sustainable is a challenge ahead.

What led to the emergence of FECOFUN?

We can identify a set of antecedent factors prompting the emergence of FECOFUN and sustaining factors helping to expand and strengthen it. Five antecedent factors are identified: democracy in1990, passing Forest Act 1993, interests and agendas of external actors, burgeoning discourse on decentralisation and devolution, and expanding role of civil society. These are briefly outlined below.

Democracy created an open environment in which citizens had the freedom to act and organise politically. This happened in 1990. Since then, an elected government and parliament were in place, creating a direct link between local citizens and the government. It was the first elected parliament after 1990 that passed the Forest Act 1993, recognising the inalienable rights of local people over forest resources. This created a foundation for the organisation of civil society around forest resources (i.e. CFUGs). Despite such enabling conditions, the immediate factors triggering FECOFUN were external actors, mainly development projects and some NGOs, who saw their interests in strengthening networks of CFUGs as a counterbalancing mechanism of power with the Department of Forest. These agencies continued to directly support FECOFUN during its formation and post-formation stages. Donors such as the Ford Foundation also contributed generously to the organisational strengthening of FECOFUN, and enabled some activists to work full time and meet the administrative costs of the organisation. The burgeoning discourse on decentralisation and devolution in the 1990s had an overarching effect at all levels of deliberations: at Parliament, Ministry of Forests and Soil Conservation, civil society, and intellectual circles. This helped to justify donor investment in networking civil society, formalising regulations supporting local management of forests, and encouraging NGOs to advocate for local people's rights over natural resources.

Once FECOFUN began to emerge, several supporting factors were also identified: committed and politically competent leadership of FECOFUN, mobilising advisory and technical services from a wide range of national and international organisations, creating a critical mass of local FECOFUN activists, holding periodic elections and creating multi-layered forums of governance, maintaining critical stance against technocratic approaches of government, and embracing an approach of inclusive self-governance. These are briefly outlined below.

The founding members of FECOFUN had long experience in political activism. They had been key local leaders of various national political parties, who fought three decades of political struggles against the autocratic Panchayat System led by the Monarchy. They brought the styles and approaches of such political activism in FECOFUN. This approach enabled FECOFUN to partially eschew from the technical rationalities and instrumental views of organisation and social mobilisation, which are common in mainstream development discourses and practices. In addition, the founding FECOFUN leaders continued to work in close collaboration with a wide network of advisors, well-wishers, and decentralisation activists. This association helped them to explore resources, analyse issues, identify strategic courses of action, and organise training and study tours for the emerging cadre base of the network.

As central FECOFUN gradually expanded its district chapters, a critical mass of local cadres emerged throughout the country, further expanding the idea and philosophy of FECOFUN. For thousands of local political workers, platforms of CFUGs and FECOFUN became attractive, partly because they are more socially acceptable institutions from which they could pursue their political interests, and partly because there was a tendency to move from politics to social sectors. Three five-year general assemblies by 2007 and four national council meetings, along with more frequent gatherings of lower committees of FECOFUN have all contributed to maintaining the integrity and dynamism of FECOFUN. The multi-layered structure of FECOFUN, with equal participation of men and women, have allowed democratic linkages between different levels and has made it possible to organise actions within different arenas.

The other factor giving life to FECOFUN is its critical schooling of its activists in issues of forest governance. Through a number of workshops, trainings, and advocacy campaigns, FECOFUN leadership has been able to cultivate critical and civilian perspective on forest governance, contrary to the historically dominant technocratic approaches. This ideology has created an alternative institution of knowledge, power and identity outside the government techno-bureaucracy.

FECOFUN's contribution to deliberative forest governance

Since its establishment in 1995, FECOFUN has been a key player in forestry sector policy development. It has consistently been pushing for citizen participation in forest management. Along with NGO alliances, it has brought civic perspectives into policy-making processes that used to be dominated by the technocratic approaches. The most important policy issue in which FECOFUN has made significant contributions in the past few years is related to the perpetuation of CFUG rights over forest resources in the hills as well as in the Terai. This included FECOFUN resistance to unwanted amendment proposals in the Forest Act 1993.

Table 4.2 provides an overview of civil perspectives which FECOFUN brought to the debate of forest policies and regulations in Nepal during the period from 1998 to 2004.

The types and range of FECOFUN activities have progressively expanded over the years. Leaders believe that FECOFUN has been able

Table 4.2   Forest policy decisions and contributions of FECOFUN in Nepal

Forest Policies and Decisions	FECOFUN arguments from civil society perspectives	Actions taken by FECOFUN
Timber Corporation of Nepal, a parastatal, granted 'one window' or monopoly rights over the sales and distribution of timber in district, as well as nationally and internationally (GON decision, 9 February, 1998)	The decision undermines development of alternative, small-scale and locally suited institutional arrangements for timber trade. There is a widespread concern over the continuing misappropriation of resources and corruption through such arrangements	Organised many protest campaigns against the mono-poly of timber corporation
1998. First Amendment of Forest Act 1993 (GON, Deceber, 1998)	The amendments of Forest Act 1993 sought to restrict some of the rights of CFUGs and give more power to DFO	Users, FECOFUN and NGOs heavily reacted upon this move and raised questions on the motive of forest bureaucracy about their faith and commitment in enhancing democratic spaces
1999. Ban on green felling(MFSC decision, 1 November, 1999)	The rights of thousands of community forest user groups were being curtailed	FECOFUN and NGOs reacted through press release, demonstrations and protests. Media highlighted the field consequences. Drew the attention of the research community and generated analyses of the issue.
2000. Circular restricting community forestry in Terai (MFSC decision, 28 April, 2000)	The handing over of the community forest were suspended	FECOFUN initiated a move-ment against the decision in collaboration with other stakeholders.
2000. Special forest policy for Terai, Chure and Inner Terai: declared new manage-ment regimes for block-system production forestry in the Terai and inner Terai, and a strict protection approach in the Siwaliks (foothills). (MFSC decision, 28 April, 2000)	Curtailing of user rights	FECOFUN launched a cam-paign demanding that Terai forests should also fall under community forestry policy and the forest near the villages must be handed over to local communities. It is the right given by the acts and legislations.

2001. Revision of community forestry operational guidelines (DoF, 2001)	Imposition of additional technicalities on CFUG's management of forest, without the accompanying delivery of needed services. Provides room for manipulating through technical reason.	FECOFUN pressurised DoF to simplify the forest hand over process
2001. An attempt for second amendment of Forest Act, 1993	Some of the rights of users were to be further curtailed.	It was heavily protested by FECOFUN and civil society and could not come into the form of bill in the Parliament. However, many of the provisions that were supposed to be amended were enacted through various decisions with Ministry (Personal communication with Dil Raj Khanal, 2004).
2002. Nepal Biodiversity Strategy (GON, July 2002)	The action plan undermined community approach to biodiversity conservation.	FECOFUN and other stakeholder protested the strategy.
2003. Government financial ordinance for levying 40 per cent tax on CFUG forest product sales (GON, 1 July 2003)	GON brought an order through Ministry of Finance (effective from 1 July 2003) without any consultation with concerned stakeholders and tried to restrict the rights of users to use their resources.	Heavy protest campaigns were organised; as a result the government reduced the tax to 15 per cent.
2003. Collaborative forest management (CFM) guideline (MFSC, 2003)	Pushed by donor projects with some token consultations. There are on going pilot projects to bring it into public sphere and deliberation through two projects (LFP and BI-SEPT) who have limited scope of facilitating process because of their modality. Debated OFMP and GON failure to implement led to come with collaborative forest management in a similar fashion of limited people participation.	FECOFUN and NGOs: Potential CF area should go with CF programme, rest can be managed through CFM but the CFM facilitation could not be managed by current level of capacity and orientation of Forest Bureaucrats. Donor projects are not viable solution to bring it into public sphere and deliberative dialogue.

Source: N Timsina *et al.*, 2004; FECOFUN (2001, 2003)

to learn a great deal from its past successes and failures in many aspects. In the past few years, FECOFUN's interventions was primarily oriented towards strengthening CFUGs and advocating for local rights in forest resources. These inputs have influenced the conditions, processes, and outcomes of forest management at the local level. An analysis of FECOFUN's activities over the past five years revealed that it has widened people's space in policy and practices of forest governance. Different ways through which it has influenced are briefly outlined below.

Raising the level of civic consciousness in forest governance

FECOFUN has created critical awareness among resource users. It is through FECOFUN that the knowledge of legal provisions related to community forestry has spread to areas where there has been no community forestry projects and where DFOs were not motivated to inform people of their rights, such as in the case of Terai. Before the emergence of FECOFUN and CFUG networks, nearly all community forestry extension services were delivered through the Department of Forest and bilateral forestry projects. The role of other NGOs was also limited until the beginning of 1990s. The federation has provided information and awareness raising services from a civic perspective which is different from that of the DFOs, projects and even development NGOs. This has helped local communities to develop a critical awareness about the forest resources, which have been constructed as 'national forest'. Awareness raising activities in some cases have been tailored to specific government plans and proposals that were considered to be detrimental to local interests and the long term sustainability of the forest ecosystem. Key messages from FECOFUN have helped to strengthen local legal and customary rights on forests. The weekly radio programme of FECOFUN has also widely disseminated ideas and information with a different perspective than conventional radio programmes sponsored by the government. Such awareness raising activities have helped to enhance the political capital of CFUGs beyond the traditional patron-client relationship with the Department of Forest.

FECOFUN has been able to extend its network throughout the country, encompassing most of the existing CFUGs in nearly all districts. This has allowed CFUGs to share experiences and ideas among themselves and learn from each other. It also aims to develop the institutional capability of CFUGs. The central-level executives of FECOFUN facilitate the networking process through its Range Post and District level networks. They raise the awareness of the district and Range Post level members, local facilitators and CFUG leaders of the importance and scope of networking. FECOFUN also facilitates the process of forming user groups, preparing operational plans and maintaining the CFUG accounts.

FECOFUN has also conducted activities that contribute to the development of institutional capacities of CFUGs, district FECOFUN chapters and local facilitators, CFUG leaders and motivators, both male and female. FECOFUN leaders and facilitators have played a crucial role in the resolution of conflicts (such as those related to forest products harvesting and distribution, withdrawal of community forests by DFOs, and boundary disputes between community forests) within and among CFUGs and other local actors.

Another capacity development service of FECOFUN is the provision of training. About a dozen types of training courses have been conducted for CFUGs and District and Range Post chapters of FECOFUN, pooling resources and trainers from within the FECOFUN system and outside. Training topics have ranged from training of trainers, forest survey, agro-forestry, CFUG formation, facilitation skills, motivation, leadership, and accounting and record keeping. Likewise, workshops on various themes such as networking, orientation of community forestry, district FECOFUN assemblies, women in community forestry, and Non-Timber Forest products (NTFPs) are regularly organised. The type and number of training programmes have further expanded in the recent years.

FECOFUN has also provided legal consultation services to member CFUGs facing legal problems. Several cases have been filed opposing the Operational Forest Management Plan (OFMP) prepared by the Department of Forest and the curtailment of local rights, transfer of community forest lands for other purposes (pers. communication with legal officer of FECOFUN). According to the FECOFUN legal officer, in the fiscal year 1999–2000, there were a total of 15 cases filed by FECOFUN at district, appellate and Supreme Court levels relating to community rights and conservation of forests and environment.

Civic resistance to non-deliberative government decisions

In several instances, FECOFUN has opposed various attempts made by the government to restrict the rights and responsibilities of forest users. For example, FECOFUN opposed the government's plan to amend the forest act 1993 as well as associated government orders and circulars that proposed several restrictions on the rights of forest dependent citizens. In this instance FECOFUN even organised a mass demonstration in Kathmandu in 2000. Similarly, it has organised mass rallies at the local level, demanding the hand over of forests as CF as per the acts and legislation (Britt 2001, Shrestha 2001). It has also organised meetings with members of Parliament and the Parliamentary Committee for Natural Resource Management to sensitise the lawmakers on the local rights over forest resources. It has submitted protest letters to the Prime Minister and the Minster of Forest and Soil Conservation, demanding the proper implementation of community forestry policies throughout the country.

The Operational Forest Management Plan (OFMP) in the Terai is another example of FECOFUN's opposition to the technocratic management of forest resources. The OFMP was prepared by technical forestry experts for the 17 Terai districts of Nepal, where the country's most valuable Sal *(Shorea robusta)* forest is available. District-wide block (relatively large continuous patch of forest) management plans were devised for government managed forests. This was criticised by

FECOUN for not providing adequate opportunities for participation of local people in planning and decision-making processes. FECOFUN's stand on this issue and the reaction of local communities actually forced the government to withdraw the implementation of the plan.

Participation in policy deliberation

Opposition to government attempts for curtailing people's rights and raising the critical awareness of ordinary people by FECOFUN have resulted into dialogical and constructive policy debates over the forest policy in Nepal. Some specific cases in which FECOFUN actively participated include (see Table 4.2): Forest Act (1993) first amendment 1998, second amendment of the 1993 Forest Act 2001 (postponed by the government), Nepal Biodiversity Action Plan, Terai (including Inner Terai and Chure) Forest Management Policy, government decisions to empower Timber Corporation of Nepal (TCN) as the single legitimate supplier of forest products, circular banning green tree felling and imposition of 40 per cent royalty on forest products sold by FUGs. In all these policy development activities, FECOFUN has clearly put forward its perspectives, given suggestions to concerned policy making authorities and, at times, strongly resisted the government decisions. Principal ways in which FECOFUN has contributed to policy processes include participating in meetings and providing critical feedback, meeting the authorities both in person and also through written petitions, and organising rallies and demonstrations.

FECOFUN has become an active participant in all key deliberations and processes of forestry at the national level, such as in the Forestry Sector Coordination Committee (FSCC) and Nepal NTFP Network (NNN). Principal forestry sector donors, such as World Bank, DFID and SDC recognise the valuable contributions of FECOFUN in bringing local perspectives to national policy processes and consequently provide them with financial support. In the past five years, FECOFUN has strengthened its presence in the agendas and programmes of institutions working in the forestry sector and the name FECOFUN is found in almost all community forestry related reports and documents in Nepal.

Influencing service delivery system

FECOFUN has influenced the strategies of service delivery in community forestry by clarifying the appropriate forest management services at the local level. Key service areas promoted by FECOFUN include group formation, institutional strengthening of CFUGs, and technical capacity building of CFUGs. FECOFUN has established collaboration with diverse groups of organisations, particularly NGOs, in facilitating the delivery of needed services at the local level.

By bridging community perspectives with other institutions, FECOFUN has influenced the agenda and priorities of institutions that provide service. It is through FECOFUN that critical areas of services needed at the local level have been highlighted. It is now commonly recognised that many CFUGs are not functioning well due to the inadequate provision of extension services at the time of formation and during the early stages of the CFUGs development.

Influencing the agenda and approaches of the political parties

FECOFUN has lobbied with political parties, lawmakers, media persons and wider civil society to establish people's rights on community forestry. Several interactions with these groups have made them aware of the importance of community forestry not only as a process of forest management, but as a model of democratisation taking place in Nepal. As such, FECOFUN has created links between the ordinary citizens and the elected politicians on matters of public concern.

FECOFUN has played key roles in sensitising local government bodies on participatory forest management and the rights of forest users. This has been particularly important in the context of nation-wide deliberations on decentralisation and local governance, and the enactment of relevant acts empowering these local government bodies to control and regulate local forest resources. As a result of interactions with FECOFUN and other NGOs, these local bodies now have a general understanding that community forestry is one step ahead in the process of decentralisation, and that they should support community forestry through CFUGs rather than interfere with it.

At the CFUG level, people hold regular annual assemblies that elect executive committees. The law has recognised only the 'group' as an entity and the executive committee as its coordination mechanism. The CFUG assembly is more deliberative than the national parliament: community forestry leaders are increasingly aware of the need to ensure that the voices of minorities, the oppressed and *dalits* are heard and addressed (Ojha and Pokharel 2006). In many groups, *Tole* (hamlet) level discussions take place prior to the assembly as regards what should be discussed in the assembly.

Influencing international developmental discourse

FECOFUN has also promoted community forestry agenda through international networking. FECOFUN leaders have participated in several international forums in the USA, Europe, Africa, Latin America and Asia, and this has helped to widely market their ideas and bring in additional perspectives and lessons. Many institutions within and outside the forestry sector have appreciated the achievements of participatory forest management. People and institutions outside the forestry sector have also started recognising that community forestry is one of the very few successful development programmes in Nepal.

All such activities have contributed to increased surveillance by local communities over the forests, and resulted in increased level of responsiveness from the Government, local bodies and civil societies to participatory forest management. In addition, intensive interactions and negotiations between the Department of Forest and local communities have resulted in a more favourable power balance between communities and government authorities, all of which are positively related to sustainable forest management. In recent years, FECOFUN's contribution has gone beyond the forestry sector and has played an important role in political movements against feudal monarchy towards establishing democratic system in the country.

Outcomes of FECOFUN actions

CFUG network development and federation building has consolidated the power of local people who depend on forests, and contributed to the reorientation of power relations between government authorities and local communities. The relationship has started changing from the traditional patron-client modality towards a form of equal stakeholders. The new power relations have made unilateral and controversial government decisions virtually unenforceable, thus underscoring the importance of pluralistic dialogues, deliberations and negotiations in forestry. The services provided by FECOFUN are critical and address the political roots of the issues and problems. FECOFUN has established itself as a constructive opposition, as well as collaborative partner, to Ministry of Forest and Soil Conservation and to the Department of Forest. This situation, in a sense, has provided a mechanism for checks and balances in the governance of the forest resources, while at the same time fostering social learning in the governance process.

Federations of forest users are an innovative example of an addition to the common property forest institutions, which are typically seen as consisting of resource user groups appropriating benefits from, and regulating access to, common forest resources. In terms of access to and dependency on forest resources, federations are positioned one step away from the CFUGs to look after issues on a larger geographic scale. The case of FECOFUN demonstrates that federations may serve three crucial functions: achievement of economy of scale (in pursuing common agendas), consolidation of power (to negotiate and safeguard interests), and sharing and dissemination of knowledge, skills and information. The pattern and types of FECOFUN interventions indicates an unequivocal focus on the consolidation of the power of the people in gaining control over forest resources.

Civil-technical knowledge interface: Key issues and challenges

Despite such massive contributions of FECOFUN in the democratic governance of natural resources, there remain pertinent challenges in its ability to learn and respond to opportunities for change. The more deliberative FECOFUN becomes internally, the more chances it has to contribute to the deliberative processes of governance nationally. This would further establish it as a democratic, transparent and accountable organisation.

Several issues are identifiable which limit FECOFUN's ability to contribute to deliberative processes in the face of continuing techno-bureaucratic challenges. First, there is still under-representation of marginalised groups. In many instances, it has been observed that FECOFUN has still to be fully owned by the member CFUGs. Despite the fact that the majority of forest users fall into the poor and marginalised categories, they are still insufficiently represented in FECOFUN committees. Although the members of the executive committee are attempting to raise their voice on behalf of these marginalised groups, hierarchical relationships within society in general prevent these interests from being properly articulated within FECOFUN itself.

The second challenge lies in FECOFUN's institutional capacity to work as a network. It inherently represents, and should ideally do so, many interests, perspectives, knowledge systems, cultural orientations and political ideologies that can be found in Nepal. FECOFUN should have a very strong internal capacity to handle such issues which are unavoidable in the discourse and practices of FECOFUN.

The third challenge is related to the emerging mindset and 'defensive routines' that are becoming embedded within FECOFUN. Interactions with FECOFUN leaders over the past several years have revealed critical insights on their attitudes and practices of deliberation and learning. Moreover, the FECOFUN leaders have been absorbed within the mainstream development/*vikase* paradigm.

The fourth challenge, although publicly declared as a federation, FECOFUN is in essence a centrally managed institution. The Nepali word *Sakha* (branch) is used to denote district committee, implying that the latter is a subordinate part of the national committee. There is no need to register the local chapters of FECOFUN independently, as they all flow from the centrally registered FECOFUN. This form of governance structure has sometimes limited the practices of internal deliberative interface. If the FECOFUN structure allows for district and lower branches in the true sense of a federation, then FECOFUN representatives would be in a better position to deliberate freely, identify new lessons and respond to citizens in a more decentralised and collaborative way.

The fifth one, following the expansion of external networks and alliances, there is a potential for FECOFUN to become externally oriented. Many local FECOFUN activists are thought to be motivated by the external opportunities rather than by their internal achievements. In the recent years, FECOFUN has been approached by an increasing number of development agencies, mainly NGOs, for collaborative works. FECOFUN leaders have themselves sought such collaborations which can allow them to implement development projects identified by NGOs or donors. There is still a significant part of FECOFUN activity which is related to delivering technical services. Such efforts in delivering technical services may divert the attention away from advancing political and civil rights agendas. From a learning perspective, it is essential to undertake research projects to understand the political and institutional conditions which limit technical research, rather than research on technical aspects per se. For example, instead of doing technical research on some aspects of forestry, FECOFUN may seek to understand why Department of Forest Resources and Survey, which has a mandate to lead forestry related research in Nepal, has actually very limited research engagement.

The sixth issue is related to financial sustainability. At present, FECOFUN has very limited resources of its own. While it depends on outside donor funded field projects for the support of the majority of its programmes and activities, it has to mobilise resources and build its capacity to raise its own funds and to function as an independent and financially self-sustaining organisation (Timsina 2003). With an increasing recognition from donors and other organisations, FECOFUN is likely to be pulled into a role of a development organisation (primarily focusing on service delivery function). From financial sustainability perspective, it is worth quoting a former FECOFUN chairman as saying "If each CFUG contributes a piece of wood to FECOFUN, hundreds of thousands of rupees can be deposited in its funds" (Timsina 2003). However, in what way FECOFUN will translate this into reality is yet to be seen. They may have a plan, but the majority of the members are unaware of it.

The seventh challenge of FECOFUN is to balance advocacy role and maintaining a dialogical relationship with the government. FECOFUN is often criticised as being too critical of the government, with limited disposition to maintain deliberative interface with the technocratic knowledge systems of forest bureaucracy. FECOFUN still has the opportunity to strategically identify and develop linkages with positive elements within government bureaucracy, and use these supportive links at the local level, influencing the priorities and programmes of various national and international organisations, local government bodies, projects and government organisations.

Conclusion

A nation-wide federation of forest users called FECOFUN has emerged in Nepal in the post 1990 democratic era to raise citizen concerns in the forest policy making processes as well as democratise practices of forest governance. Two key conditions favoured the emergence of this largest civil society network in Nepal. First, the government was forced to seek the cooperation of local people in halting deforestation in the Himalayas. Second, the opening up of civil spaces after the introduction of multi-party representative democracy widened the scope of civil actions. The evolution of FECOFUN is indeed a citizen led initiative to create a constant frontier of deliberation between the forest dependent citizens and technical forestry experts. While the intensity and quality of deliberation in forest policy making has improved significantly as a result of FECOFUN, uncertainties exist with regard to FECOFUN's institutional capacity to handle its internal challenges of accountability, intra-organisational democracy and deliberation, and administrative capacity.

Acknowledgement

We thank Bhola Bhattarai of FECOFUN for his valuable comments and factual corrections. We are also thankful to various central committee and district committee members of FECOFUN for their insightful engagement with us on the working of FECOFUN. Our colleagues, Krishna Paudel, Ram Chhetri and Basundhara Bhattarai have also given helpful comments on the draft. We thank Scott Robbins for his editorial support. The framing of this case from deliberative governance perspective was made possible by two research projects – Research on Knowledge Systems of ForestAction, and Adaptive Collaborative Management Project of ForestAction and CIFOR, both funded by IDRC. The authors take full responsibility for the views and arguments.

References

Argyris, C. (1993). *On Organizational Learning*. Cambridge, MA: Blackwell.

Backstrand, K. (2004). Scientisation vs. Civic Expertise in Environmental Governance: Eco-Feminist, Eco-Modern and Post-Modern Responses. *Environmental Politics*, 13(4): 695–714.

Blaikie, P. M., J. Cameron and D. Seddon (2001). *Nepal in Crisis: Growth and Stagnation at the Periphery*. Oxford: Clarendon Press.

Britt, C. (2001) 'Mixed Signals and Government Orgers: The Problem of on-Again off-Again Community Forestry Policy. *Forests, Trees and People Newsleter*, 44: 29–33.

Chambers, S (1996). *Reasonable Democracy: Jurgen Habermas and the Politics of Discourse*. Ithaca and London: Cornell University Press.

Dryzek, J. S. (2000). *Deliberative Democracy and Beyond: Liberals, Critics, Contestations*. Oxford: Oxford University Press.

FECOFUN (2001). *Report of Third General Assembly of FECOFUN.* Kathmandu; Federation of Community Forestry Users, Nepal.

FECOFUN (2002). *Report of Third National Council Meeting.* Kathmandu: FECOFUN.

FECOFUN (2003). *Report of the Fourth National Council Meeting.* Nepalgunj: FECOFUN.

FECOFUN (2001). *FECOFUN letter to Didi Bahini* (date - 2058/7/6, letter no - 83/058/59), Federation of Community Forestry User Groups, Nepal.

FECOFUN (2003 (2059)). *Report of the Fourth National Council Meeting.* Nepalgunj: Federation of Community Forestry users, Nepal.

FECOFUN (2007). *The Constitution of FECOFUN.* Kathmandu: Federation of Community Forestry Users, Nepal.

Fischer, F. (1999). Technological Deliberation in a Democratic Society: The Case for Participatory Inquiry. *Science and Public Policy,* 26 (5): 294–302.

Fischer, F. (2000). *Citizens, Experts and the Environment: The Politics of Local Knowledge.* Durham and London: Duke University Press.

Forester, J. (1999). *The Deliberative Practitioner: Encouraging Participatory Planning Processes.* Cambridge, Massachusetts and London, UK: The MIT Press.

GON/MFSC (1995). Forest Act 1993 and Forest Regulations 1995. Kathmandu: Government of Nepal.

Hobley, M. (1996). *Participatory Forestry: The Process of Change in India and Nepal.* London: Rural Development Forestry Network, Overseas Development Institute.

Kanel, K. R. and B. R. Kandel (2004) Community Forestry in Nepal: Achievement and Challenges. *Journal of Forest and Livelihood,* 4 (4): 55–63.

Malla, Y. B. (1997) Sustainable Use of Communal Forests in Nepal. *Journal of World Forest Resource Management,* 8: 51–74.

Ojha, H (2002) *Users' Federation in Forestry: Emergence, Interventions and Contributions to Sustainable Community Management of Forests in Nepal.* Discussion paper, Forest Action Nepal, Kathmandu.

Ojha, H. and B. Pokharel (2006). Democratic Innovations in Community Forestry – What Can Politicians Learn? *Participation,* Nepal Participatory Action Network.

Ojha, H. (2006). Techno-Bureaucratic Doxa and the Challenge of Deliberative Governance – The Case of Community Forestry Policy and Practice in Nepal. *Policy and Society* 25 (2): 31–75.

Parkins, J. and R. Mitchell (2005). Public Participation as Public Debate: A Deliberative Turn in Natural Resource Management. *Society and Natural Resources,* 18(6): 529–540.

Peluso, N. L. (1992). *Rich Forests, Poor People: Resource Control and Resistance in Java.* Berkeley, Los Angelos and Oxford: University of California Press.

Pokharel, B. and H. Ojha (2005). *Community Forestry in Nepal: A Platform for Public Deliberation or Technocratic Hegemony?* Brisbane: International Union for Forestry Research Organisations.

Regmi, M. C. (1977). *Landownership in Nepal.* Delhi: Adroit Publishers.

Roth, R. (2004). On the Colonial Margins and in the Global Hotspot – Park-People Conflicts in Highland Thailand. *Asia Pacific View Point,* 45 (1): 3–32.

Sarin, M. (2005). *Laws, Lore and Logjams: Critical Issues in Indian Forest Conservation.* Gatekeeper Series. London: International Institute of Environment and Development.

Sarin, M., N. M. Singh, N. Sundar and R. K. Bhogal (2003). *Devolution as a Threat to Democratic Decision-Making in Forestry?* Findings from Three States in India. London: ODI.

Shivaramakrishnan, K. (2000). State Science and Development Histories: Encoding Local Forestry Knowledge in Bengal. *Development and Change,* 31: 61–89.

Shrestha, K. (1999). Community Forestry in Danger. *Forests, Trees and People Newsletter* (38): 33–34.

Shrestha, N. K. (2001). The Backlash – Recent Policy Changes Undermine User Control of Community Forests in Nepal. *Forest, Trees and People Newsletter,* (44): 62–65.

Shrestha, N.K. and C. Britt (1997). 'Crafting Community Forestry: Networking and Federation-Building Experiences.' *Community Forestry at a Crossroads: Reflections and Future Directions in Development of Community Forestry.* M.L. Victor, C. and Bornemeier, J. (eds.) Bankok Regional Community Forestry Training Centre. pp. 133–144.

Smith, G. (2003). *Deliberative Democracy and the Environment.* London: Routledge.

Sundar, N. (2000). Unpacking the 'Joint' in Joint Forest Management. *Development and Change,* 31: 255–279.

Sundar, N. (2001). Is Devolution Democratisation? *World Development,* 29 (12): 2007–2023.

Timsina, N. (2003). Viewing FEFOFUN from the Perspective of Popular Participation and Representation. *Journal of Forest and Livelihood,* 2 (2): 67–71.

Timsina, N., H. Ojha and K. P. Paudel (2004). Deliberative Governance and Public Sphere: A Reflection on Nepal's Community Forestry 1997-2004. *Fourth National Workshop on Community Forestry (548-558).* Kathmandu: Department of Forestry, Nepal.

Young, I.M. (2003). 'Activist Challenges to Deliberative Democracy.' *Debating Deliberative Democracy.* J.S. Fishkin and P. Laaslett (eds.) pp. 102–120 Oxford: Blackwell.

5

From Isolation to Interaction: Increasing Knowledge Interface in *Chhattis Mauja* Irrigation system in Nepal

Laya Prasad Uprety

Introduction

The chapter focuses on perception, production, communication and application of knowledge by the farmers while managing an indigenous irrigation system. The data generated were form a fieldwork conducted in *Chattis Mauja* indigenous irrigation system (CMIS) located in the plains of Rupandehi district in western Nepal. The population in the command area is characterised by cultural and caste/ethnic diversity and despite this, the irrigation system has been effectively functioning for a long time and is often cited as an example of the participatory and sustainable irrigation system in Nepal. Ethnographic methods like key informant interviews, field observation and household census were the principal data-gathering tools. In addition, focus group discussion was also used.

Nepalese farmers have recognised the importance of water resources for centuries and have been constructing irrigation systems at their own initiatives to augment agricultural yields. This tradition has given birth to Farmer Managed Irrigation Systems (FMISs). Historically, irrigation development has fallen under the domain of a religious trust, individual initiatives and/or community effort. The legal tradition and local administrative structures over a period of time have permitted FMISs to operate without interference from an irrigation agency or administrative unit. However, they have been assisted by the government from time to time when natural calamities required resources beyond the capacity of the farmers (Paradhan 1989; Pradhan and Bandaragoda 1998).

A substantial portion of the country's irrigated area is under numerous FMISs scattered across the country. About 950, 000 hectares of arable land in the country have some form of irrigation, of which 675,000 hectares are under FMISs and 275,000 hectares are developed and managed by government agencies. FMISs account for over 70 per cent of irrigation development in the country and contribute over 40 per cent of the national cereal crop production (Poudel *et al.* 1997).

Overview of *Chhatis Mauja* irrigation system

Chattis Mauja irrigation system was originally constructed by the Terai autochthonous *Tharu* people. Initially, it served a total of 36 *Maujas* as the command area, and later expanded to other villages covering 3,500 hectares. At present, there are more than 3,900 irrigator households in its command area. Key informants reported that the system was built during the time of the Prime Minster Jung Bahadur Rana about 170 years ago. Local *Tharu* leaders had received the land grant from the Rana Prime Minister for the reclamation of land and generation of revenue. The completion of the canal construction took approximately three years, which could irrigate 36 *Maujas* (villages) and was accordingly named *Chhattis Mauja* irrigation system. It was also called Kumari Kulo (Kumari canal) because it irrigated the villages located in the vicinity of Kumari area. In the early days, mobilisation of labour was led by the local *Jamindar* on compulsory basis until the completion of the work.

After the eradication of malaria in the late 1950s, the influx of the hill migrants increased in the command area which also resulted in the expansion of the command area in the 1960s and 1970s. In 1960, a joint Indo-Nepal agreement was reached for the development of another irrigation system in the area by using the water of Tinau River, which created a condition for the two irrigation systems, namely, *Sohra Mauja* and *Chhattis Mauja*, to share the water diverted from the same headwork. Until then, the diversion of *Sohra Mauja* was located in between the northern side of the head of the existing canal and the southern part of the *Barro* tree in Tinau river. As per the Indo-Nepal agreement, the government of India began the construction of dam for the new irrigation system in 1962. In doing so, the new dam of *Sohra Mauja* permanently closed down and it adversely affected the irrigation facilities of the farmers.

Victimised by the work of developing the new irrigation system, representatives of the farmers of *Sohra Mauja* assembled and visited the then zonal commissioner of Lumbani Zone and filed a petition protesting the negative effect of the construction work of India and requested for fixing the new *Mohda* (the water diversion location) for the canal from Tinau. The authorities of both India and Nepal were very sympathetic towards the farmers of *Sohra Mauja*. Then, in the process of fixing the *Mohda*, the concerned officials and technicians from Nepali and Indian side including representatives of the farmers made a meticulous on-site inspection and developed, a new understanding between *Sohra* and *Chhattis Mauja* systems for sharing the water through a single mega-canal from the new common headwork location (which was originally used exclusively by *Chhattis Mauja*). The administrative letters issued by the office of the zonal commissioner of Lumbini in 1966 have corroborated this fact.

The location for the proportionate division of water between *Sohra* and *Chhattis Mauja* had been fixed by the Chairman and secretaries of *Sohra-Chhattis Mauja* joint management committee (which was formed after they had to start sharing the water), and other village notables at a place called Immilihawa in 1965. But when the representatives of the joint committee and executive committees of *Sohra* and *Chhattis* gathered at a place called Jogi Kuti Immilihawa for the discussion for opening the proportioning water dividers, the representatives of *Chhattis Mauja* argued that the permanent water divider be opened at a place called *Tara Prasad Bhond* since a couple of *Maujas* such as Dinganagar and Siddhanagar of *Sohra Mauja* had taken water from that location. The representatives of *Sohra Mauja* accepted this suggestion and the permanent proportioning water divider was opened at *Tara Prasad Bhond*. Both side also agreed that 60 per cent of the total volume of water running in the single mega canal be allocated to *Chhattis Mauja* and the remaining 40 per cent be allocated to *Sohra-Mauja*.

In 1986, the *Sohra-Chhattis Mauja* joint committee made a joint decision to construct a permanent regulator at the *Tara Prasad Bhond* for the division of water with the support of the external agencies. Under the top-down irrigation development model, little attention was paid to the self-sustaining FMISs. However, it has been ascertained that the *Chhatis Mauja* irrigation system had received cash, materials, technical assistance and equipment contributions occasionally in the past from the external stakeholders such as the department of irrigation and local governments. All this was used for the improvement of the main system including the construction of the concrete proportioning weir to resolve the problem of the division of water between the two systems. Thus, there are complementarities of the indigenous practices (such as diverting water using stone crates, bushes and sand) and dividing water between the two systems through the permanent proportioning divider constructed with the use of modern technology.

It is also important to analyse the distribution of the irrigator households by caste/ethnicity in the six sample Maujas of the irrigation system. The data shows that majority of the irrigator households (65.5 per cent) are *Brahmins* followed by the *Chhettris* (14.8 per cent). Though the area was predominantly settled by the *Tharus* prior to 1960s, the social composition dramatically altered thereafter and now they constitute a minority in the command areas. It was revealed by local informant that with the influx of hill migrants, many of the *Tharus* left their *Maujas* and settled closer to dense forests in the vicinity where they could live in a homogeneous community.

The data on irrigator households also revealed that an overwhelming majority (89.7 per cent) of them were hill migrants. Though migration of people from hill to the *Chhattis Mauja* command area began in the early 1940s, the influx of migrants is said to have increased after 1960s once the endemic malaria was eradicated. Some of the migrants are also from the neighboring *Terai* districts such as Nawalparasi and Chitwan while others have come from Burma when the Nepali population could no longer live there due to political changes in early 1960s.

The key informants suggested that migration had an impact on the irrigation system. This comprised: the leadership of the farmers' organisation which was generally taken over by the hill migrants. The original *Maujas* of the head location became the tail-end *Maujas* (because there was a lot of land for reclamation above the original ones). Other changes included codification of the traditional irrigation norms/rules/ regulations into the form of the constitutional choice' for governing the behaviour of the growing irrigators with diverse social and cultural backgrounds, disappearance of the traditional *Tharu* cultural practice known as *Sidhabandi* for the maintenance of the headwork and the upper part of the canal. More cash and labour mobilisation took place for repair and maintenance of the main canal and its distributaries due to the growth of the irrigators and consensual decision for the change in timing for the annual repair and maintenance work of the main canal and its headwork which changed from May-June to February-March.

Despite the fact that the head and middle location of the command area has been increasingly urbanised within the last two decades, majority of the irrigator households (63.6 per cent) still practice agriculture as the main economic activity. However, field survey shows that the degree of dependence on agriculture as the main source of income varies from *Mauja* to *Mauja*. There are households in the command area which have adopted non-agricultural activities as the primary source of income such as small-scale business, carpentry, masonry, running tea-stalls, government and private sector services, recruitment in the British and Indian armies and overseas employment mainly in the middle-east, and East Asia. Such households consider agriculture as the secondary source of income.

The average size of the land holding in the study area is 17.29 *Katthas* (0.57 hectare), which indicates that the farm holdings are relatively small. Nonetheless, the average agricultural land holding varies from one *Mauja* to another ranging from 11.35 *Katthas* to 24.73 *Katthas*[9]. Paddy is the principal cereal crop grown followed by wheat and maize. Farmers also grow the legumes, potato and oilseeds. The key informants pointed out that over the last 30 years, there have been changes in the practices of agriculture. For example, the indigenous varieties of paddy have been replaced by the improved varieties developed by the government agricultural research centres. Prior to 1970s, the *Tharus* used to broadcast the paddy seeds but this is not practiced any more. People have resorted to using the tractors in lieu of the traction animals. Maize and wheat were introduced only in the mid-1960s. The agricultural produce has easy access to the local markets – a function of the growing urbanisation and transportation facilities.

The economy is predominantly subsistence-oriented but the field observation has shown that farm work is given less importance by the educated youths who prefer white-collar jobs and overseas employment. This is so because on the one hand, the fragmented holdings do not absorb all the working hands and on the other hand, there is a perception among the settlers that agriculture as a profession is not that remunerative given the high cost of production inputs. The landlords who had owned large tracts of land had absolute power in the community in the past since the only source of income was land. These landlords were called the *Jamindars* whose function was to encourage and bring the settlers for reclaimed land for agricultural purposes and collect revenue from

---

[9] One *Kattha* is 0.0339 hectare and twenty *Katthas* constitute one *Bigha* (0.6772 hectare).

the farmers on behalf of the state. The cultivators had to depend on the mercy of the *Jamindars* and non-compliance with his order used to result in harsh punishments or eventual eviction. Thus, power was relational. The *Jamindars* exercised control over land resources and it followed as a corollary (in the past) that the cultivators/settlers were mobilised by the *Jamindars* for the development of irrigation system. If the farmers did not comply with the rules for the contribution of labour, they even had to be ready to quit the *Mauja* since they could be evicted in extreme cases. Farmers failing to pay the *Khara* in cash had to pay in kind in the form of castrated goats, oxen and utensils. Failure to pay in kind would result in confiscation of these animals and commodities by the *Jamindars*. In the feudal structure, the farmers were dependent on local *Jamindars* in a number of ways such as land renting-in, and obtaining financial loans and therefore, compliance with the irrigation rules was a must.

The *Tharu* community has a traditional community leader called *Badhghar*. In the past, he was very powerful because he was responsible for the dispensation of justice and management of the community development works including the management of the irrigation. He was supported by a *Chaukidar* (watchman who used to work as a messenger and his assistant). The *Chaukidar* was accountable to the *Jamindar* for the community level developmental works and therefore was responsible for the mobilisation of the labour for the annual, periodic and seasonal repair and maintenance works of the irrigation system.

The management of irrigation-related works has continued under the leadership of a committee elected by the general water users. And the new leadership has been exercising its power over the farmers through the appointment of *Meth Muktiyar* and village level *Muktiyars* who basically execute the system level and *Mauja* level decisions respectively for the sustainability of the irrigation system.

Ever since the advent of the multi-party system in 1990, the community-based organisations (CBOs) have been largely affected by partisan politics. There are instances when these organisations have been used along political party lines by the elected functionaries and conflict has been a regular phenomenon. The candidacy for the post of the principal functionaries of the system level executive committee is often based on political party lines. This can also generally happen at the lower level of the organisation. But once the election is over, the organisation and its lower level units basically function apolitically.

Anyone assuming the post of the chairperson of the *Chhattis Mauja* is recognised as an important civil society leader at the national level because she/he represents one of the largest and most sustainable farmer-managed irrigation systems. For example, the ex-chairman of the system had once been elected as the chairman of the national federation of the water users' associations – a very prestigious position. She/he can influence the decision-makers at the national level for the larger interest of the farmers. Thus, there has been change in the political dimension of irrigation management.

Knowledge systems in *Chhattis Mauja*: Innovations in technical, organisational, institutional and governance arrangements

Technical arrangements

The river Tinau is the source of the *Chhattis Mauja* irrigation system and its volume of water fluctuates greatly from monsoon to dry season. At the head of the Butwal municipality, the river changes from narrow to wide banks and enters the lowland plain, depositing large boulders and heavy silt, making water acquisition for irrigation extremely difficult. This irrigation system is a run-off river gravity flow using a temporary brush diversion along the upstream portion (563m) which is changed and reconstructed by the farmers each year according to the fluctuations in the water volume. In the winter when water level in the Tinau is low, the brush diversion is extended upstream as far as the local farmers think necessary to capture sufficient water. The length of the brush diversion is reduced and shifted downstream by the farmers during the rainy season due to high volume of water (IIMI 1990).

The total length of the *Chhattis Mauja* canal is 14 kilometres from the diversion intake of Tinau river to the tail-end location of the command area. There are two temporary intake structures constructed by the farmers at places called Kanyadhunga and Ittabhond along the bank of the river. They are located at a distance of approximately 1.5 kilometres from each other. The intake structure at Ittabhond has been constructed using the stone crates. At the same location, an iron gate for controlling the excess water has also been installed but this has not yet been made functional. With the collaborative efforts of the farmers and the government, an escape structure upstream of the same gate has also been constructed. The water from both the temporary intake structures is mixed and divided between *Sohra Mauja* and *Chhattis Mauja* at a place called *Tara Prasad Bhond*, which is located approximately one kilometre downstream from the temporary intake located at Ittabhond. There is permanent proportioning dividing weir at *Tara Prasad Bhond* where the ratio of the distribution of water for *Chhattis Mauja* and *Sohra Mauja* is 60:40 respectively.

Farmers have also constructed *Sanchhoes* (proportioning weirs) for the division of water between and within the *Maujas* from the main canal. These are generally stable concrete structures. But in the past, they were of temporary nature made up of locally available materials such as bushes, wood, sand, soil and stones. Based on their traditional local knowledge, the proportioning weirs are such that they are designed to allocate water, which is approximately proportional to the amount of the land available in a particular *Mauja*.

Organisational, institutional and governance aspects

Crafting the institutions by framing a constitution would be regarded as documenting a process of collective knowledge on the procedure of governing the behavior of the irrigators. The organisational, institutional and governance aspects of the irrigation system have been well covered in the constitution. The operational rules for irrigation in the past were based on the 'oral tradition'. Based on the prevailing practices, the water users of *Chhattis Mauja* had first drafted their constitution in 1981 and revised it in 1991 and 1994 for regulating the behaviour of the irrigation users in the changing context.

The preamble of the constitution states very clearly that the users of this system have the pride for being the exemplary reference for others using indigenous management systems. The expansion of the command area over the years and the need to seek the necessary financial and technical co-operation from within and outside the country for improving the irrigation system, mobilising the labour of the water users properly, helping the farmers accrue more benefit from agriculture and bringing the organisation of the water users within the institutional framework are the principal factors addressed in the constitution.

E Ostrom (Ostrom 1996) is of the opinion that appropriation, provision, monitoring, enforcement, conflict resolution, and governance activities in common are organised in multiple layers of 'nested enterprises'. Irrigators can be organised at three or four levels. In fact, the organisational structure of the irrigators of *Chattis Mauja* is four-layered, viz, the joint committee of the *Sohra – Chhattis*, main committee, regional committees, and *Mauja* level committees.

Given the fact that the farmers of *Sohra* and *Chhattis Maujas* have been using the same joint dam since 1965, they have formed a joint committee comprising 11 members, six nominated members from *Chhattis Mauja* and five members from *Sohra Mauja*. The functions of the joint committee include pulling the financial and material resources from the external agencies/organisations, maintaining the co-ordination between *Sohra* and *Chhattis Mauja* for the sustained operation, ensuring the right of 40 per cent and 60 per cent of the total water from the main canal to *Sohra* and *Chhattis* respectively, mobilising the cash and labour resources for the upkeep and maintenance of the main canal.

The *Chhattis Mauja* irrigation system as an enterprise is organised in the form of a federal organisational structure. There are village level, area level and the main system level organisational structures. General meeting is held once a year. But the main committee can call its meetings any time to make decisions on any complicated subjects. Formulation of the policies, regulations, study of the account audited, approval of annual income and expenditure, election of the chairperson, vice-chairperson and member secretary of the executive committee, making final decisions on the issues raised by the executive committee and contribution to the formation of committees/sub-committees/issue-based commissions are the major functions of general meeting. All the expenses are also to be approved by the general meeting.

The general assembly is another important organisational arrangement to make policy decisions. The chairperson or *Mauja Mukthiyar* (chief official of the village) or representative of the *Mauja* (village) elected by the majority of the water users of each *Mauja* and the members of the main executive committee constitute the general assembly. In terms of apropos of the quorum of general meeting and general assembly of *Chhattis Mauja*, 51 per cent of the total members should be present for the first time. The executive committee formed by the general assembly discharges the day-to-day functions of the organisations on behalf of the water users. The tenure of the executive committee members is of two years.

The system has the institutional provision of appointing the staff for undertaking irrigation-related activities under the guidance of the executive committee. *Meth Mukthiyar* is the principal staff supported by two assistants for work as directed by the executive committee. More specifically, he mobilises labourers for *Kulahai* (which is the specification of the amount of repair and maintenance work of the main canal on the basis of the size of the command area of each *Mauja*) and takes their attendance regularly, gives the *Nath* (measurement of the part of main canal) for *Kulahai*, mobilises labourers for the emergency *Kulahai* without the permission of the committee (if the main canal structure is broken or during the special circumstance but the committee has to be informed about such *Kulahai* within three days), decides the rotational distribution of the water among the several *Maujas* by considering the timing of the farming and distributes it accordingly, supervises water distribution, and reports to the chairperson the case of the person/*Mauja* who/which violates the rotational norms of water distribution with evidences, and discharges other official works with the support of two assistants. Interestingly, there is also the provision of having a *Mukthiyar* and *Chaukidar* in each *Mauja* who are also remunerated but the remuneration varies from *Mauja* to *Mauja*[10].

In *Chhattis Mauja*, there is also the provision of *Gaun/Mauja Muktiyar*. The *Gaun/ Mauja Muktiyar* (village level functionary selected or elected by the irrigators) is responsible for disseminating the decisions of the village level committee apropos of its activities. There is a provision to fine her/him, if she/he fails to disseminate the information or communicate the decisions on time including the fines or other fees to be paid by the irrigators. There is also the *Gaun Chaukidar* (village level watchman) who has to comply with the orders of the *Gaun/ Mauja Muktiyar*, regional representative and executive committee (as per the necessity). He has to give information regarding *Mauja* to the *Mauja* level committee and the information of the *Mauja* level committee has to be given to the irrigators. He also supervises the rotation of water distribution within the *Mauja* and the condition of branches/tertiary/water courses of the *Mauja* and assists the *Gaun/Mauja Muktiyar* in discharging his roles. He also works to maintain cordial relations between the *Mauja* level committee and *Mauja Kularas* through furnishing the necessary information on time.

It is important to distinguish between allocation and distribution in the study of irrigation. U Pradhan (Pradhan 1989) agrees with Martin and Yoder (Martin and Yoder 1987) that water allocation and distribution are the distinctive important functions for any irrigation system. Water allocation is the assignment of water from an irrigation system and this has two dimensions. The first dimension distinguishes the farmers or

---

[10] For example, the *Muktiyar* of Kumari *Mauja* is paid NRs. 4000 per year and the *Chaukidar* is almost invariably paid in kind. He is exempted from the *Kulahai* for one *Bigha* of land (0.67 ha) and receives five kilograms of paddy from each irrigator household. In addition, the *Mauja* level committee also provides a flashlight, a pair of water boots and an umbrella every year.

fields having access to the system's irrigation from those not having such access. The second dimension is determination of the volume of water to be allocated in the system among the farmers or the fields.

It is the water users or irrigators who have a better understanding on the indigenous collective knowledge developed in the past and handed down to them by their ancestors. This given them the right to appropriation water for irrigation in the *Chhattis Mauja* system can only be claimed by those households with landholdings within the command area and contributing to the maintenance of the irrigation system. It has been reported that the number of *Maujas* appropriating water varies each year. Those contributing to the resources for the regular repair and maintenance of the system are recognised as the member *Maujas* and the non-contributing ones are immediately denied their membership rights. Thus, the farmers have good deal of understanding that the contribution is the basis of the creation of property rights in the irrigation system.

The farmers of the *Chhattis Mauja* irrigation systems have set their own norms for water allocation. *Kulara* is the basic water allocation unit. The prevailing local cultural definition of one *Kulara* is 25 *Bighas* of land. Each *Mauja* is required to send one labourer for the repair and maintenance as and when needed per *Kulara*. Traditionally, each *Mauja* has the right to claim a fraction of the total discharge of water flowing in the main canal. In February – March 2003, 56 *Maujas* had a total of 152 *Kularas*. The data provided by the main executive committee revealed that the number of *Kularas* per *Mauja* may fluctuate periodically and this may not always same because of the amount of land in each *Mauja*. For an example, the amount of the land of some *Maujas* is less compared to the number of the *Kulara* and it is vice versa in other *Maujas*.

Distribution is the actual delivery of water to the fields of the farmers. There has been institutional arrangement for the equitable distribution of the water between and among the farmers of a particular *Mauja*. When water is abundant it flows regularly in all the branch canals which are proportionate to the number of *Kularas*. *Meth Muktiyar*, *Mauja Muktiyars*, and the functionaries of the executive committee gather and decide the proportionate distribution of water to each *Mauja* on the basis of the number of *Kularas*. But when there is scarcity of water in the main canal, each *Mauja* receives water for certain hours as per *Kulara* on rotational basis.

Within the *Mauja* also, water flows in all the territories, water courses and field channels during the period of abundance. But there is a schedule of water distribution during the period of relative scarcity such as winter season. Water is distributed from the outlet of the field channel as per the contribution by the households for *Kulahai* on the basis of the landholding. Water distribution pattern also depends on the type of the crops. For example, few households grow wheat and maize which do not require much water and there is no problem within the *Mauja* during the cultivation of these crops. But during the period of paddy nursery bed preparation disputes between farmers for access to irrigation water tend to be common and the *Mauja Mukthiyars* and *Chaukidars* have to work very hard to settle them.

The *Chhattis Mauja* irrigation system has a democratic culture in decision-making. At the *Mauja* level, all the users have the opportunity to have their say during the time of general assembly. Their voices, regardless of the caste/class status, are heard by the concerned functionaries and staff. If any genuine problem related to irrigation, resource mobilisation or any other related work crops up during the discussion of the general assembly, decisions are made immediately in a participatory way. *Mauja* level committee and the *Mauja Muktiyar* makes every effort to resolve the local disputes and problems within the *Mauja*. But if it cannot be resolved at the local level, this is communicated to the higher level committees.

The general meeting and the general assembly are also important forums for making decisions where the representatives of the farmers from all the *Maujas* participate. In these forums, every representative has the opportunity to articulate clearly the inter-systemic, systemic, inter-*Mauja* and intra-*Mauja* irrigation-related problems and actively contribute to the process of decision-making. The decision-making is in the control of local community and therefore, their legitimate interests are generally fulfilled.

The resource mobilisation for the regular and emergency maintenance, water allocation and distribution are communicated to the *Mauja* level committees and *Mauja Muktiyars* by the *Meth Muktiyar* with the support of his assistants. Once this is done, the *Mauja Muktiyar*, with the support of the *Mauja Chaukidar*, disseminates the information among the irrigators of the *Mauja*. For example, the decisions made by the *Mauja* level committee are communicated to the *Meth Muktiyar* or the functionaries through the *Mauja* level *Chaukidar*. The complaints lodged by the irrigators at the *Mauja* level (if they cannot be solved locally) are also communicated to the executive committee/*Meth Muktiyar* in the same way. The nine regional representatives also work as the link of communication between the *Mauja* level committees and executive committee. The decisions made by the executive committee that potentially affect both *Sohra* and *Chhattis* are also communicated to the joint committee and its *Meth Muktiyar* through the assistants or *Meth Muktiyars* or other functionaries of the executive committee who represent the system in the joint committee. Depending upon the gravity of the problem/issue, both written letters and verbal means of communication are used. The *Meth Muktiyar* of the joint committee communicates the message to the *Meth Muktiyar* of *Chhattis Mauja* on the regular and emergency maintenance work and the necessary resource mobilisation for the main canal above the *Tara Prasad Bhond*. The decisions of the joint committee (as per the necessity) are also communicated to the executive committee in a formal way.

Mobilisation of the resources (both internal and external) is a must for the sustainability of any irrigation system. The irrigation organisation predominantly mobilises the internal financial resources for which the sources include fines collected in case of non-compliance of rule, regular fees collected from the farmers and financial support received from external agencies. The sand/gravels of the main canal can be sold by the executive committee and the income from such sales also belongs to the funds of the irrigation system. Apropos of it, the executive committee can also conclude the contracts with the buyers. The *Mauja* level committee can also do the same.

There is an organisational norm of having an audit committee which appoints a recognised auditor and gets all the accounts of the yearly income and expenditure audited. The financial report prepared is presented to the general assembly by the main committee.

The water users have developed their own indigenous system of conflict management. Three levels of conflicts are found: inter-systemic conflict, inter-*Mauja* conflict, and intra-*Mauja* conflict.

Conflicts between and among the *Maujas* are also the common sociological phenomena in this irrigation system. The conflicts between the head, middle and tail locations arising from the violation of the distributional norms do occur frequently and such cases are generally mediated by the system level executive committee upon the lodging of the complaints by the affected parties conflict resolution is done through an on-the-spot inspection, persuasion, and creation of a conducive environment for compromise between the conflicting *Mauja* parties. The decisions are accepted by the conflicting parties.

Intra-*Mauja* conflict is also very frequent. The principal sources of such conflict include the violation of water distributional turn, water theft, unjust distribution of water between head, middle and tail farmers. When conflict arises between and among the farmers of the head, middle and tail locations or between and among the farmers of a particular location, the issue is brought to the *Mauja Muktiyar* by the affected party/ies who then make the immediate on-the-spot observation. During the period of observation, the conflicting parties are allowed to present their arguments. The witnesses are also called for verification of the conflicting complaints. Once the complaints of the conflicting parties and the opinions of the witnesses are heard, the *Muktiyar* tries to persuade the conflicting parties and resolve the issue through compromise. But if he fails to resolve the issue of the conflict, it is brought to the *Mauja* level mass meeting which then finalises the case through elaborate discussions. The person/s responsible for the infraction of the irrigation norm has/have to accept the decisions including the compromise/ payment of the compensations to the affected party/ies settled by the majorities in the *Mauja*. If any *Mauja* develops a diversion of the watercourse from the main canal at its own disposal by severely affecting other *Maujas* and steals water, compensatory fines are imposed by assessing the level of negative impact. For the first time, the fines would be NRs. 1000, NRs. 1500 for the second time, and NRs. 3000 for the third time. And if the trend of non-compliance continues, the maximum punishment could be inflicted upon it by closing the diversion of water from the main canal for a specific season or for the whole year. This norm is also applicable to the case of violating the rotational turn of water of each *Mauja* by any other *Mauja*. But the norms of *Mauja* are also applied in the case of the violation of water rights of the farmers within the *Mauja* which are decided by the functionaries of each *Mauja*.

Knowledge systems interface: Insights from *Chhattis Mauja*

Given the fact that CMS users have realised that they cannot remain in isolation for sustaining the irrigation system, they have interacted with a multitude of actors by interfacing/negotiating/deliberating. These comprise: techno-bureaucrats, political party leaders, development agencies including NGOs and wider civil society networks. They have come into contact with the techno-bureaucrats because they needed a reliable rational technical intervention support for the division of water from the single canal between two irrigation systems. The farmer leaders also needed the institutional strengthening support from the techno-bureaucrats. Given the fact that the command area is a significant political constituency, political leaders, both in the past and the present, have shown interest to support the system to win the favor of irrigators during the election of local and national governments. Equally important is the fact that leaders of the irrigation organisation also have a propensity to approach the political party leaders for support during the resource-crunch situation for maintenance of the system with the intention of capitalising locally available political resource. Indeed, the leaders of irrigation organisation have always known that their support is also crucially important for the political leaders to win the elections, be they local or national. Therefore, the political leaders are willing to contribute the critical cash and material support from the funds of local governments or pressurise the line agency of the central government for the release of necessary funds. In the past, a few Nepali researchers had conducted studies on this irrigation system and they have now set up NGOs which are reported to be occasionally supporting the system for its institutional strengthening. Finally, the interface with the wider civil society networks is the function of having a dynamic and active institutional leadership in the past which was very influential for advocating the rights of farmers at the local, regional and national levels.

Empirical data have shown that these interfaces have unequivocally supported the irrigation system for effective functioning. Given the fact that farmers are aware of the positive effect of the collaborative institutional efforts, whatever technical, economic and institutional supports were offered by the techno-bureaucrats, political party leaders, and development agencies have been regarded as instrumental in making the water distribution reliable and equitable on a sustained basis. For instance, the construction of the proportioning weir for the division of water between two irrigation systems has almost eliminated the conflict in the allocation of water through improvised structures. So is the result of institutional support which has enabled the leaders of irrigation organisation to negotiate with external actors for regular or additional resource support.

The actual processes of negotiation between the local irrigators and the various groups of external agents took place when there was the starkest need for external support. The farmer leaders sought the collaboration of external agencies when maintenance of the irrigation system was generally inadequate through the utilisation of local resources.

Discussions in the preceding sections have show that local irrigators have developed their own systems of organising technical and institutional processes based on their own perception and knowledge of the local social and ecological realities. As a result, they have been able to organise diverse forms of inputs such as labor, cash and locally available materials to the regular, periodic, seasonal and emergency maintenance of the system. They have also contributed collectively to the evolution of the organisational and institutional arrangements for the governance of the behaviour of irrigators. The nested organisational structure of the farmers represents the legitimate interests of the irrigators on the one hand, and works to control the free-riders by enforcing the rules developed collectively by the irrigators on the other hand.

Despite its autonomous pursuit of action and knowledge, there are diverse fronts in which local irrigators have to negotiate knowledge, power and resources. This external interface has both supportive and constraining effects in the local irrigation system. There are at least four different types of knowledge interfaces.

First, the institution is seen by local politicians as worthy capturing, and therefore party factionalism is reflected in the election of the various positions in the system. Material support from local and national governments are negotiated with the partisan interests.

The local government is another category of the local level stakeholders who generally support the irrigation system with the material and financial resources. For example, many Village Development Committees (VDCs) have provided the stones from their financial resources to the irrigation organisation for the construction of the retaining wall along the alignment of the main canal. The District Development Committee helped the irrigation system by providing support in kind (such as the grains for the sale to generate the cash) for the improvement of the main canal.

Second, as the technical system experienced difficulties (such as through siltation, and water division devices), local irrigators have resorted to scientific knowledge interface. The Government department has provided necessary devices, along with training. These have worked well.

The role of the government is also critically important in supporting the irrigation system by providing the technical assistance, material support and the financial resources for the construction of stable structures. This work was very capital-intensive and required technical skills from the engineers. The government also provides dozer (free of cost) for de-siltation of the head location of the main canal at the request of the irrigators' *Sohra-Chhattis* joint committee. In the absence of such support from the government, de-siltation at the diversion of the canal would require a large number of the labourers from the irrigators. The per diem of the driver and cost of the fuel are borne by the organisation. Operation of this support activity was observed during the fieldwork of this study. In fact, the farmers' organisation has been requesting the government for its support to construct a permanent dam at the head of the main canal which has not materialised so far. The Department of Irrigation has also been supporting the organisation for its institutional strengthening by means of training and workshops.

Third, the local irrigators have increasingly been affiliated with higher order networks of water users (WUA), which has helped local irrigators to understand their own political rights and obligations, thus contributing to increased deliberation over policy and practices of FMIS.

Given the fact that this irrigation organisation is also a member of the National Federation of the Water Users' Association (WUAs), it has also been playing an active role for raising the genuine voices of the farmer-managed irrigation systems (FMISs) at the district and national levels. In the past, the ex-chairman of the *Chhattis Mauja* irrigation organisation had been the chairman of the national federation of WUAs who had been leading the national campaign for the promotion of the interests of the FMISs by influencing the policy makers. In this way, there exists a relationship of this organisation with a host of similar community – based resource organisations at the district and national levels.

It thus appears that CMIS is coming into increasing number of knowledge interfaces for enhancing the technical, institutional and political effectiveness of the system. This is indicative of the fact that resource management cannot be looked at in isolation. The sustainability of the resource management system is possible provided the resource appropriators have been successful in maintaining the relationships with other multiple actors and stakeholders.

Conclusion

The farmers of *Chhattis Mauja* irrigation system have created tremendous amount of local knowledge over time on irrigation technology, institutions and organisational structure for its effective functioning. The collective knowledge created at the local initiatives by the ancestors and handed down to the generations through the culture of 'oral tradition' has been adapted as per the need of the users either by using their own wisdom or through an interface with other knowledge systems. This indicates that the collective indigenous resource management knowledge has to be dynamic.

It is observed that if the community is homogenous and relatively small, it is relatively easier to govern the behaviour of the resource appropriators, which is possible through strict observance of the customary rules. Monitoring the behaviour is also possible because everyone knows everyone. But when the demographic and social composition of the resource appropriators is heterogeneous and relatively large, then there arises a need for codifying customary rules into the form of constitutional – choice arrangements, which helps create a larger formal structure with the representatives of appropriators for governing their behaviour.

The present research has shown that the knowledge created at the local initiatives can help sustain the resource management. The irrigation system is more 170 years old but it has been operating as a successful example of the farmer-managed irrigation system. It would be safe to generalise that the existing knowledge of the resource management has to be capitalised and built upon while giving the development interventions for the resource management and this would eventually contribute to the sustainability. The *Chhattis Mauja* is one of the perfect examples of the successful governance through the development of multi-scale organisational structure in the most democratic fashion and evolution of the institutional arrangements through the use of collective knowledge of the farmers.

The irrigation development policy makers have to be mindful of capitalising the existing social capital (i.e institution and organisation) while formulating the policy for the modernisation or improvement or rehabilitation of existing indigenous irrigation systems. By doing so, they can save both time and resource needed for creating and sustaining new social capital for the governance of the behavior of farmers utilising water for irrigation. Farmers would also have the sense of ownership if their existing organisations and institutions are mobilised and strengthened right from the very beginning of modernising or improving or rehabilitating the existing indigenous irrigation structures.

The irrigation policy makers, planners and programme implementers should also create a congenial environment for farmers' organisations to function independently which, in turn, triggers the evolution of grassroot democracy or democratic governance practices. Definitely, such environment eventually leads to the sustainability of irrigation management.

Given the fact that the local knowledge for any resource management is the accumulation of historically and ecologically tested ideas and practices through collective endeavour, it is highly sustainable and therefore, the irrigation policy makers, planners and programme implementers have to recognise it and build upon it for ensuring farmers' ownership and sustainability. Farmers also have the potential of being the gurus to the modern rational technologists, policy makers, planners and programme implementers which is definitely opposed to western notion of so-called 'scientific knowledge' regime.

Each knowledge system has its deeply-embedded cultural value and has the potential to be complementary to each other for any effective and sustainable resource management effort, which, eventually, has its bearing on the improved livelihood of farmers of the developing countries on a sustained basis.

References

Agrawal, A. (1995). Dismantling the Divide between Indigenous and Scientific Knowledge. *Development and Change*, 26 (3): 413–40.

Agrawal, A. (1995). Indigenous and Scientific Knowledge: Some Critical Comments. *Indigenous Knowledge and Development Monitor*, 3 (3): 3–6.

Brokensha, D., D. Warren, and E. Werner (eds.) (1980). *Indigenous Knowledge Systems and Development*. Lanham, MD: University Press America.

Chambers, R. 1983. *Rural Development: Putting the Last First*. London: Longman.

Coward, W. (1986). Direct or Indirect Alternatives for Irrigation Investment and the Creation of Property. In.Easter, K.W (ed.), *Irrigation Investment, Technology, and Management Strategies for Development*. Boulder, Colododo: Westview.

Durga K.C and U. Pradhan (1993). Indigenous Knowledge and Organisational Process: Experiences and Lessons from Local Nepali Irrigation Systems. In D. Tamang, G. Gill and G.B. Thapa (eds.), *Indigenous Management of Natural Resources in Nepal. Policy Analysis in Agriculture and Related Resource Management*. Kathmandu: Ministry of Agriculture/ Winrock International.

Gilmour, D.A and R. J. Fisher (1992). Villagers, Forests and Foresters. Kathmandu: Sahyogi Press

IIMI. 1990. *Rapid Appraisal of Irrigation Systems*. Kathmandu.

Martin, E. and Yoder, R. (1983). 'Review of Farmer Managed Irrigation in Nepal', *Water Management in Nepal*, pp. 88–91, Ministry of Agriculture, Agricultural Project Services Center and Agricultural Development Council Inc.

Ostrom, E. (1996). *Governing the Commons: The Evolution of Institutions for Collective Action*. Cambridge: Cambridge University.

Pieterse, J.N. 2001. *Development Theory: Deconstructions/Reconstructions*. New Delhi: Vistaar Publications.

Poudel, R.A., Shukla,. N.R. Joshi, S.M. Shakya and D.N. Yadav (1997). Understanding the Dynamics of Rehabilitation Processes: Lessons from the East Rapti Irrigation Project. In: Shivakoti, G. et.al (eds.), *People and Participation in Sustainable Development. Understanding the Dynamics of Natural Resource Systems*. Rampur: Institute of Agriculture and Animal Science, Tribhuvan University.

Pradhan, P. 1989. *Patterns of Irrigation Organisation in Nepal*. Colombo: International Irrigation Management Institute, Sri lanka.

Pradhan, P. 2003. *Eroding Social Capital through Incompatible Legal and Institutional Regimes: Experiences from Irrigation Systems in Nepal.* Workshop in Political Theory and Policy Analysis. Bloomington, Indiana: Indiana University.

Pradhan, P. and D.J. Bandaragoda (1998). "Legal and Institutional Environment of Water Users Association for Sustainable Irrigation Management" in *Irrigation Association for Participatory Management in Asia* (pp. 31–47). Bangkok: Asian Productivity Organisation.

Pradhan, U. (1998). *Local Resource Mobilisation and Government Intervention in Hill Irrigation System in Nepal.* Washington D.C: Consortium for International Development.

Royds Consulting Ltd, Rural Development, Inc., Consolidated Management Services Nepal Pvt. Ltd. and Multi Disciplinary Consultants Pvt. Ltd. (2000). *Nepal Irrigation Sector Project Irrigation Subsidy Study.* Phase II Report. Kathmandu, Nepal.

Sillitoe, P. 1998. The Development of Indigenous Knowledge: A New Applied Anthropology. *Current Anthropology,* 39 (2): 223–235.

Tamang, D. 1993. Challenges and Opportunities in Farm and Community Resource Management in Nepal. In D. Tamang, G.Gerald and G.B. Thapa (eds.) *Indigenous Management of Natural Resources in Nepal.* Policy Analysis in Agriculture and Related Resource Management. Ministry of Agriculture/ Winrock International Press, Nepal.

Tang, S. Y. 1989. Institutions and Collective Action in Irrigation Systems. *PhD Thesis.* USA: Indiana University.

6

Action Research Experience on Democratising Knowledge in Community Forestry in Nepal

Mani R Banjade, Harisharan Luintel and Hari R Neupane

Introduction

Nepalese society has historically been socially, economically and culturally diverse and differentiated. However, the Hindu and patriarchal cultural production of knowledge has been dominant throughout the history and has created social inequities and injustice within the society that is manifested in unequal power relations, which are defined by caste, class, gender and regional settlement. These diversities have further created the islands of knowledge communities and value systems of those sections of the society. Poor, women, ethnic minorities and people of remote locations have historically been excluded from mainstream state politics, bureaucratic positions, and denied proportional representation by the government. In the process, feudal mindset and historically constructed social power has legitimised the knowledge of local elites (usually they are from rich and higher caste people) and bureaucrats in every aspects of social life including natural resource management.

In this broader context of the society, forests have been centrally managed by the state from late 1950s. So far the state and the forest bureaucrats have overly relied on the technical and colonial knowledge of forest management. The state has tried to protect the forest by alienating the people from it despite local people's indispensable dependence over the resources. However, the state could not protect the forest from encroachment, deforestation and resource depletion. Simultaneously, there were many successful cases of indigenous knowledge based forest management practices in the remote and rural parts of the country from the long past. Both these conditions have prompted the search of community based alternative modality for the sustainable and equitable management of forest resources.

Community forestry is considered one of the best alternatives for sustainable forest management in Nepal. Advocates of community forestry argue that it offers the best prospects for the inclusion of the poor, women, *dalit* and marginalised people, augmenting local level livelihood capitals while promoting the sustainable management of forests. However, inequity in community forestry has existed in multi-dimensional forms and at different scales and intensities (Banjade 2003; Malla 1999, 2000, 2001; Malla *et al.* 2002; Neupane 2000; Hobley 1987, 1996; Barraclough and Ghimire 1995; Pokharel 1997; Timsina 2002, 2003; Paudel and Ojha 2002; Ojha *et al.* 2002). These inequities along with other second generation issues such as forest governance, livelihood contribution of CF and sustainability are realised not only due to the result of the existence of *ad hoc* and top-down decision-making processes in both the communities and facilitating institutions but also due to the limited knowledge base of the policy makers and the planners about the communities' diversity in demand of the forest products and differentiated access and control over forest management decisions. At the same time, there is over domination of the Department of Forests and donor agencies at the national level and local elites at the community level due to the power generated through policy, knowledge, and culture.

Institutional arrangements and processes being used in promoting community forestry are also being questioned, as these do not usually include the poor and marginalised in the decision-making process (Neupane 2000). Even the widely used Participatory Rural Appraisal (PRA) tools, have been criticised because they are often used without proper understanding of the existing power relationship of the communities and thus further reinforce existing exclusions and inequities (Cooke and Kothari 2001). These issues have been pressurising policy makers, planners and practitioners to search for inclusive processes and structures in community forestry. To this end, not only what knowledge and skills are required to facilitate the processes but also whose knowledge and whose stake in the politics of constituting/reconstituting the knowledge, are important. More democratic and interactive processes are thus, desirable in ensuring equitable forms of governance and management in CF. Bottom up decision-making systems based on the knowledge of stakeholders involved in both communities and the supporting institutions can provide some space for knowledge interface.

Increasingly, there is a strong pressure for the inclusion of the poor, women and marginalised groups within community forest user groups (CFUGs) in decision-making and benefit sharing. In order to have democratic legitimacy of knowledge, it should hold basic principles like truth, trust and accessibility to all and should serve users' interests particularly to create more benefits. In this chapter the authors seek to address the question of how different social actors (members of various caste, class, gender and ethnicity) of a community with diverse interests, knowledge and power interact and collectively learn to develop socially and set up, rules and social practices for the management and use of natural resources. Drawing lessons primarily from Participatory Action Learning (PAL) conducted in four CFUGs of Nepal, the chapter critically examines how knowledge and power relationships among social actors have created the conditions and processes of equitable forest management practices. The analysis of empirical data provides insights on how a series of reflective and deliberative discussions among actors can promote redefining and negotiating political spaces for themselves as well as determines institutional arrangements for forest management and benefit sharing.

Participatory action learning in community forestry

A total of four CFUGs were selected for a detailed study. These groups represent different geographical locations (both the Hills and Terai) and socio-economic heterogeneity (defined by gender, class, ethnicity, geography). The characteristics of each study CFUGs are given in Table 6.1.

The CFUGs under study differ in terms of history of forest management practices. While Sundari and Gagankhola CFs have been managed recently by a group of migrated people, Baishakheshwori and Karmapunya CFs have been managed by local inhabitants since long past. Similarly, the opportunity of external interface varies on the basis of prevailing contexts. For example, Sundari and Gagankhola CFUGs received higher external interface due to adjoining east-west highway and market access than Baishakheshwori and Karmapunya CFUGs.

All the CFUGs selected for the purpose of facilitating PAL were characterised by weak communication between the executive committee and users and also among users. Despite the recognition of Sundari, Gagankhola and Baisakheswori as relatively better CFUGs in the respective districts in terms of their governance, environmental conservation and livelihoods contributions, the issues of exclusion and elite domination in CFUG processes persisted in all the four CFUGs. The poor, women and *dalits* were structurally excluded to hold key positions in executive committee (EC). More specifically, the decisions of the CFUGs were influenced by a single leader and/or executive committee with limited deliberation. Majority of the users were unaware of the decision-making processes and hence showed low level of interest to get involved in forest management. In these CFUGs, power and knowledge of elites had become legitimate and ordinary people did not question the authority. Since there was limited space for interaction,

Table 6.1 Some relevant characteristics of the CFUGs under study

S. No.	Name of CFUG	Address	Region	CF Area (ha)	HH	Ethnic Composition	Key Characteristics	PAL duration
1	Sundari	Amarapuri – 1-9, Nawalparasi	Western Terai	390.0	1268	Brahmin, Chhetri, Gurung, Magar, BK.	Timber oriented forest management, one man leadership	2003–April 2006
2	Gagankhola	Lalpur-2 & 5, Siraha	Central Terai	75.0	165	Pasawan, Rai, Yadav, Mahato, BK.	One man leadership, committee domination, exclusion of poor, lack of transparency	2003–2005
3	Baisakhesowari	Mirge-9 & Jiri-1, Dolakha	Central Hills	102.85	155	Sherpa, Chhetri, BK, Newar.	Passive forest management, lack of ideas regarding resource management	2004–April 2006
4	Karmapunya	Bhimkhori – 1-5 & Mechhe 5, Kavrepalanchok	Central Hills	321.4	325	Chhetri, Tamang, Newar, Dalits, Magar.	Limited exposure with external stakeholders, poor governance	August 2003–2005

the possibility of generating new knowledge and use were obstructed in the CFUGs. In addition, there was differential access to decision-making and benefit sharing for men and women belonging to various class and castes.

Approach and action steps adopted for facilitating action-learning

ForestAction, an NGO active in the field of participatory action learning, played an important role in facilitating the learning process in these CFUGs. The facilitators (the authors) considered the reflective and critical investigation approach for focusing on collective analysis of the past and existing situations as well as making a vision plan for the future. The focus was on the learning outputs of the process in order to create an environment towards the exploration of emancipatory knowledge through putting to practise the vision plan. While doing so, we considered the identification of problems/issues and their root causes, which consequently capacitated the users of the CFUGs to address such problems. The process reached beyond the elite group to the general users so as to ensure their contribution in decision-making. This in turn enhanced the outcomes of CFUGs in terms of social justice particularly equity concerns, CFUGs' internal governance, forest management and ultimately the livelihood of the users including forest dependant poor people. The facilitators encouraged the users to create a forum for interest negotiation that could recognise the different segments of the community on the basis of various parameters such as wealth, caste, regional settlements and gender.

The facilitators followed different steps while facilitating CFUG level PAL. These steps were evolved during the process of facilitation and negotiation among different stakeholders (including individuals and sub-groups) within the CFUGs. These steps constitute 'learning cycles' which are crucial in generating shared knowledge and using them in future course of actions. A learning cycle involves an iterative series of steps such as situational analysis, planning, action, monitoring and reflection/learning leading to the next cycle of planning, action, monitoring and reflection (see Fig. 6.1). Although the broader steps appeared to be more or less same in all the four CFUGs, the forest users themselves, given the variation and diversity in ecology, socio-economy, politics and culture of the society, identified a number of sub-steps to be followed in order to democratise power and knowledge relationships.

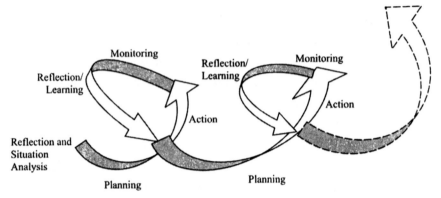

Fig. 6.1   Continuous Learning Cycle of Planning, Action and Reflection (adapted from Hartanto *et al.*, 2003)

There are four different action steps adopted during the process of facilitation which were as follows:

Step 1: Reflecting upon the situation: understanding the context

a. *Informal meeting with the CFUG committee members*

Initially, the facilitators organised an informal meeting with selected committee officials as well as some general members in all sites. During the meetings decisions were made to organise various meeting with different stakeholders to reflect upon the governance of CFUGs in terms of sharing power and knowledge for resource management and for designing various forms of institutions to manage conflict and collaboration. Holding several informal meetings with the key officials was useful for exploring the context of the CFUGs.

b. *Formal meeting with CFUG committees*

The objective of this step was to explore the overall situations of the CFUG committees in terms of knowledge and power relationships along with other issues in the way the committee members perceived and played their role in forest management as well as take consent to work closely with the group. The facilitator(s) put various questions to the EC members in groups and individually in critical and reflective ways. The EC members were questioned on equity and social justice, participation, ensuring benefits from CF to the poor and marginalised can be benefited from the community forest and the role and responsibilities to be played by the EC in order to become more accountable and democratic.

After putting the critical questions from the facilitators, members of EC were able to reflect on the issues of the CFUG, including their governance and the institutional mechanisms obstructing the achievement of the expected social change. They reflected that participation of users in general assembly (a policy making forum at village level in relation to forest use and management) was limited as most often poor, *dalit* and women did not have any information about the assembly. In most of the cases, the chairpersons and secretaries of the committees seemed to be active in the management process and they paid little attention to the opinions of other users (as other members were also passive) in decision-making process. Most of the committee members were also not much aware about the activities such as financial transactions. Committee members and the users appeared to have little knowledge about their rights and responsibilities too.

> Prem Kumar Lama, one of the EC members, said "a number of visitors have been visiting our forest and we have a policy to charge some entry fee to them. But, we do not have any idea, how much money has been received by our committee and how it has been spent".

A number of tensions and conflicts were observed while facilitating the process. For instance, Treasurer of Gagan Khola CFUG committee stated: "I do not know any transaction of this CFUG although I have been given the responsibility of treasurer. Only Chairperson and secretary take decision related to financial matter. Most of the time, the CFUG committee meeting ended with no decision. Users concerned are rarely heard".

After a long discussion with the EC members, they agreed and decided to conduct the hamlet (*tole*) level meetings to seek opinion of all villagers. These meeting sites were decided on the basis of accessibility. The reflective questions in relation to equity, justice and livelihoods opportunities raised by the facilitators in these meetings resulted in engaged discussions that eventually allowed the members to reach a new level of knowledge on the subject.

Step 2: Analysis and planning

To have an in-depth understanding of the CFUG processes and institutions, the facilitators also had meetings with key informants, such as women and poor household members of the group. The information received was analysed and shared with others.

c. *Holding meetings at toles*

Several small *tole* meetings were conducted over several days with the participation of the majority of households in order to understand the opinion of the users regarding the management of the community forests. The *toles* were grouped into clusters that made it easy for people to participate in the *tole* meetings. Moreover, individual level communication was held between the users and committee members that led to an increase in the participation of users in the discussions. Each participant was given opportunities to put forward his or her ideas related to governance, communication, forest management and so on. Most of the participants claimed that these meetings made it possible for them to know about what was happening to their forest management (particularly creation of knowledge).

Reflections of critical issue at tole meeting

In case of Gagan Khola CFUG, users and even the treasurer do not know the financial transaction of the group and the EC still appeared to be reluctant to make it public. In second case, the CFUG fund has been used to develop the drinking water facility in the village. But the rich and powerful people in the village decided to fix taps for personal use (they even used for irrigating kitchen garden) whereas the poor and marginalised especially so-called *dalits* have a single tap in a *tole* (among many households), which is inadequate for them. Since the poor and marginalised group have little or no say over the decision making process, they possess low bargaining power that have created such gaps both in knowledge and power. The third case, some of the users has been provided opportunity to cultivate the aromatic plants (grasses) in the forest area. However, the poor households could not get benefit from the sale of products, as the cost of the production is higher than the sales value due to 25 per cent levy imposed by the EC on the sales price.

To start with, EC members were requested not to interfere in the discussions[11], so that the *tole* residents feel comfortable to make comments against the office bearers and committee members. The issues for discussions included benefit sharing mechanisms, the implication of decisions taken by the EC, rules and regulations of CFUGs, individual contribution to community forestry development and fund mobilisations. All participants were allowed to express their views turn by turn. The facilitators observed that some of the young people were more emotional, a number of elderly and marginalised were aggressive whereas the women in general were found to be less influential and shy while speaking. However, two women who were in the EC of Karmapunya CFUG expressed their observations: "They (women and poor) could speak so openly in today's meeting. It was wonderful. We never experienced women of this village speaking in that very way. You know, in our yesterday's meeting also women were not saying much even though only women of the *tole* participated in the meetings".

---

[11] Our assumption was that the EC members are of elite class and have a sort of informal and formal control in the decision making in the village and in the community forestry development process. The poor, marginalised, women and *dalits* generally do not speak against EC members.

Almost every one expressed dissatisfaction with the CFUG committees decisions and working procedures. People showed strong willingness to be involved actively (if recognised and provided with opportunity) in the community forestry development process and make contributions. Most of people raised questions about the issues directly related to their livelihoods, utilisation process of the forest products, mobilisation of the fund as well as governance transparency in decision making process, responsiveness and accountability of the CFUG committee compliance of the rule of law and participation of the marginalised sections of the society.

Tole meetings were found to be useful for creating knowledge and power on individual needs and concerns and thereby encourage marginalised people to speak up and become organised for future actions. Two representatives (one male and one female) were selected at the *tole* meetings to represent these *toles* in larger forums. The concerns raised in these forums were documented carefully and crosschecked during the meeting. Many users agreed to share the document incorporating all issues with the EC members (in a workshop setting) in detail.

Men and women seemed to have different interests on managing the forest in terms of use, for instance, men appeared to be interested in timber production and while females liked to focus on daily-use forest products such as fuelwood, grasses and leaf-litter. Similarly, *dalits* wanted to be liberated from social oppression, while some of the other upper caste people blamed the facilitators for taking side of the *dalits*. Poor and rich also had different interest in forest management. For instance, mobilising CFUG funds, the rich people wanted community development like drinking water supply, roads, irrigation, whereas the poor wanted soft loans for income generating activities. Poor, marginalised and *dalits* were trying to advance their interests but others were not in favour of them, although they appreciated the involvement of these people in decision making.

d. *Workshop with tole representatives and executive members*

A workshop of *tole* representatives and the EC members in each CFUG was organised in order to discuss individuals' and *tole* level concerns. The *tole* representatives shared the issues and problems raised during the *tole* meetings. However, some of the *tole* representatives were not able to put their critical views in the *tole* meetings. Basically, the *tole* representatives appeared reluctant to speak against the EC members and other elites of the villages because of their domination and strong hold in the existing socio-economic structures. The workshop was crucial in making the *tole* representatives aware about the concerns of other *toles* and getting organised to tackle the problems likely to be faced in the workshop of *tole* representatives and the EC members. We learnt that in a situation of elite domination and unequal power relationship, it is important to have a separate interaction of less powerful groups prior to interface for interest negotiation. The discussion as such would help develop synergy on their knowledge and thereby develop strategies of negotiation with EC.

For the purpose of addressing the problems/issues raised during the *tole* meetings, the issues were grouped into three broad categories namely social justice, governance and technical aspects in order to make contributions to policy formulation process while reforming the constitutions and forest operational plans of the CFUGs. The workshop sensitised the participants in realising the principle of social justice into practice. The workshop formulated three different sub-committees to perform various jobs: policy shaping sub-committee to formulate the poor-focused policy at local level, finance sub-committee to make all the previous financial transactions transparent to the user group during the general assembly, and general assembly preparations sub-committee to call the users and manage all the logistics.

During the interaction, some of the EC members pointed out that the facilitators were biased towards the poor and marginalised which was indeed very challenging task for the facilitators. The contradiction and tensions expressed by the participants with differential knowledge and power were also observed during these workshops. *Tole* representatives such as Kale BK and Sushil Paswan said, "the committee members undermined the need of the users and trying to avoid the voice of *tole* representatives. They still are not ready to listen to the poor and marginalised. We are now here for asserting the need of local people and make our voice heard in the decision making process". In response to them, Rajeshwori Rai, an elite member of a *tole* replied, "those who are poor became poor with their own behaviours. They get drunk and are lazy. They are mostly untouchables and it was their fate to be poor".

e. *Reflection at the tole level*

The outcomes of the joint workshop of *tole* representatives and the CFUG committee were shared within users in the *toles*. Suggestions, options and opinions were received for further refinement of the proposals. For example, the sub-committees reflected that the medium and/or rich categories of users still depend on forest resources to some extent; their rights should not be undermined in the name of the poor focused programme. Thus, they tried to promote community's agendas in general within which nested poor-focused agendas envisioned as first priority. Learning from the interaction and reflection, a few practical options to address the existing problems were discussed and documented.

f. *General assembly*

According to the Forest Act 1993, the general assembly of CFUG is the most powerful and legitimate body to make decisions and determine directions for change within the CFUG. The proposals developed through earlier steps/processes were put forward in the assembly for discussion, adaptation and decision. In our study sites, the assemblies approved new group constitutions and forest management plans and also reorganised the EC. The assembly set procedures for effective communication, deliberation, enforcement of rules and decisions, self-monitoring and learning. The general assemblies were organised in the communities with necessary logistic and other preparation in all four CFUGs. The participants were seated *tole*-wise and in half-moon shape so all users had opportunity to see, listen and put their voices in the plenary for making good decisions from the assembly. At first, a formal session was organised followed by informal session and zero hour for further discussion in each CFUG.

Recognition of powerless and dominated

A *dalit* (untouchable) and poor widow chaired the general assembly of the CFUG. She felicitated all members of the group and provided flowers to all participants as a token of gift as the chief guest of the programme. In Hindu religion, it was not easy to accept a *dalit* and poor woman as the chairperson of any programme in a caste ridden society. The action learning process adopted in Sundari CFUG has raised awareness and created critical knowledge about the emancipation of the people from the domination. It appeared to be useful approach in creating democratic and justifiable knowledge that facilitated to change the existing power relationships among the people. However, a few Brahmins (elite users) did not accept her as the chair of the programme and left the assembly. But majority of the people appeared to be happy with a change in the relationship of power.

When the chairpersons and treasurer presented the progress and financial report of the CFUGs, each *tole's* users were allowed to make comments separately. There were mixed reactions on the report presented. Users raised several questions on the use of funds and asked for clarification on the ways the funds had been used. These questions literally created a difficult situation for the committee. However, users ultimately approved the report on the condition that the CFUG committees keep all the transaction transparent in future. For example, in Gagan Khola CFUG, once the policy formulation sub-committee presented the draft policy, some of the rich and elite people who had informal power in the community opposed the policy and argued that the proposed policy focused primarily on the interests of the poor and overlooked the interests of other users. They presented an alternative draft, which had less focus on the poor. The users seriously discussed and debated on both the draft policies and ultimately they reached a consensus that favoured the poor and marginalised users. However, a proposal forwarded to provide the revolving loan without interest to the selected poor (exclusively) for the income generating activities was rejected by the general assembly. In the case of Sundari CFUG, the case was different.

Step 3: Putting decisions into action

g. *Action group formation for implementation*

Action groups were then formed according to the approved plans. Plans were also drawn up for review of the ongoing activities and for continued reflection to facilitate learning from actions, including failures, and interactions effectively.

Step 4: Reflection and learning

h. *Self-monitoring and reflection*

At this stage, CFUGs were encouraged to make necessary arrangements to institutionalise a review of the ongoing activities and continuous reflection to facilitate the learning process. This step was realised as vital, where the users were able to judge the achievements and learn more expected outcomes when they observed and reflected upon from the results of their actions. In the action learning process, failures were recognised as opportunities to learn, eventually reducing the shock of failure. The monitoring and reflection process was important for users to analyse the contextual information that was collected during the process, and use the same to improve further planning. When collective learning process was practiced, it was likely that different knowledge systems deliberated to form new knowledge which could become more legitimate and less discriminating to the marginalised users.

i. *Follow-ups*

Follow-up actions, regular monitoring and feedback mechanisms were developed to facilitate the reflection – planning – action – monitoring – reflection/learning cycle to continue in the CFUGs. To support this, each of the steps suggested above were monitored and reflected upon. Information thus received would be analysed so as to maximise the learning at each level. The outside facilitators would follow up on the process over the course of the next cycle, while local facilitators would lead the process.

Equity outcomes of the action and learning processes

In all four sites, knowledge and power gaps were obvious. Before the process, the representation of poor and women users in the decision making process was negligible. If they were represented, they did not have voice; if they expressed their voice, they were not heard. The practice of benefit distribution from the forest was not based on the needs of the users. In most of the cases, the poor and marginalised users were not aware of their rights and responsibilities to forest governance. During the CFUG formation period, the DOF field staff and their practices had excluded these marginalised groups including women. This systematic intervention study process helped to raise awareness of the people where poor and marginalised were actively engaged in producing and communicating the knowledge.

Inclusion of the excluded

The users from each *tole* select their representatives to the CFUG committees that include all categories of users including women, *dalit* and poor. However, lobbying was facilitated in favour of selecting the poor, marginalised and *dalit* so as to enhance the access of those categories in formal decision-making forum. Then an additional decision making authority was given to the selected members with the condition that at least 50 per cent women should be in major decision making positions such as chairperson or vice-chairperson and secretary or treasurer. After this intervention, the processes of CFUG committee formation seem more representative and democratic as compared to the earlier situation when it used to be formed haphazardly under the influence of few elite users. The process detected an error in previous practice in forming the CFUG committee, and facilitated an effective action that corrected the error by establishing a systematic mechanism to include the excluded. Though it seemed somehow threatening and embarrassing for the already powerful stakeholders, it was useful to change the *status-quo* in the community.

Creating the bridge between EC and the users: A mechanism for knowledge interface

A decision has been taken to regard the *tole* representatives as permanent bridges between EC and the users. *Tole* representatives are responsible for maintaining the smooth communication between ECs and users as well as ensuring the participation of the users in the forest management and community development activities. They are also responsible for providing feedback to the EC by monitoring the activities of the committee. The bridging mechanism appeared to be more useful in providing information and generating knowledge for policy framework.

Example of positive discrimination

A lower caste member, showed his disagreement on the existing distributional system of treating all categories of users equally, rather he was more concerned with positive discrimination in favour of poor members of the CFUG. He gave a concrete example of timber distribution and claimed that poor users should get timber at lower prices than those of relatively well off users.

Making a mechanism for regular monitoring

There was need to establish a mechanism for regular monitoring from and within the CFUG. For this purpose, monitoring sub-committees other than EC members were formed. The sub-committee regularly and closely observed and analysed the functioning of the ECs and users as a whole and provided feedback to them. The monitoring action is not only required in order to act effectively, it is also necessary in order to codify effective action, so that it can be reliably used in other circumstances as learning from experience can be claimed as creation of new knowledge.

Equity-based forest product distribution system

The reformed constitutions of the CFUGs articulated the knowledge and power dynamics in a better way favouring the poor and marginalised. For example, in Sundari CFUG, 25 households were identified as poorest of the poor through wealth ranking and the CFUG assembly decided to provide free membership and firewood free of cost to them. Similarly, in Gagan Khola CFUG, ten households were identified as poorest of the poor and EC decided to support them. Moreover, a provision was made to provide firewood free of cost for the purpose of cremation for all the users irrespective of economic classes considering the socio-cultural value of Hindu funeral rite. In Bishakheswori, 16 households were provided CFUG membership and community forestland for income generating purposes.

Contested knowledge and deliberative interface

Democratising knowledge is a political process, which includes redistribution of power and benefits. Taking community forestry as example, we could find that the links between resources and people are so intricate, complex and dynamic that it involves technicalities of management as well as politics of resource governance. Therefore, any effort to promote equity in a complex system of community forestry should be informed by a broad understanding of social and political processes (along with biophysical systems). The mainstream resource management practices in CFUGs still seem to make policy decisions without adequate analysis and consultation with the poor, not moving beyond the current situation of elite domination. PAL, however, challenged it and drew up a strategy for inclusion of the excluded. Particularly, interface of external facilitators with existing leadership, and small group meetings of users (*toles* and sub-groups) contributed towards providing more space to the poor, women and *dalits* in the decision making processes.

In all study sites, there was limited interface taking place between the social agents (men and women, poor and rich, *dalit* and non-*dalit*, outsiders and insiders), which appeared to be constraining to create critical knowledge and change the power relationships. The knowledge of powerful people becomes legitimate and often unquestionable. In this context, the planned intervention with reflective approach provided a platform for all to bring their agenda into public. Sometimes the community with a certain knowledge system may not appreciate the other knowledge systems and may stick to their own limited knowledge. They may think that their knowledge is the truth.

The *tole* level interactions in four CFUGs appear to be the main hub of communication for local people. The interactions among the users and committee members at different levels led to the social learning for all stakeholders at local level that proved to be a useful process in understanding the relationship between human and nature as well as changing the relationship between the users. The special focus to empower the poor and marginalised involves a rigorous political process which also will sensitise the power elite at the local level as has been reflected in the *tole* meetings and subsequent interactions between the members of user committee, *tole* representatives and the users.

In recent years, issues related to equity, justice, governance and sustainable development have become the knowledge variables in community forestry. However, the knowledge base of both the theory and practice remained the same that appeared to be major constraining factors in achieving intended objectives. In this context, PAL has explored a practical and innovative approach for democratising and transforming knowledge and power dynamics at community level. As argued in the theoretical framework of this book, the critical knowledge generated through the PAL process proved to be the means of emancipation of poor and marginalised from domination and sub-ordination by the existing social structures. It has also generated some insights on the political aspects of resource management that how actors at different layers of governance with unequal power and authority, can engage in negotiations for equitable knowledge outcomes.

Community forestry involves forest resource, users of it who are directly linked to it for their livelihood, and external agents who have some stake on the management of the same (might include service providers and market agents). There is always a debate on which of these actors should have dominant roles in producing, using and legitimising the knowledge of resource management and group governance. Looking at the community forestry policy processes in Nepal it is being observed that local voices and knowledge are inadequately appreciated and used while producing, enforcing and revising national policies (Ojha, forthcoming). Role of external agents is highly influential in challenging the existing paternalistic and discriminatory knowledge of some powerful people against the marginalised ones (Banjade and Ojha 2005; Banjade *et al.* 2006). In societies operating under unequal knowledge and power relations, involvement of external facilitators in PAL process can provide a critical interface of local (indigenous) and external (scientific) knowledge and contribute positively in democratisation of knowledge. In the studied CFUGs, for example, with support from capable external facilitators, collectively produced knowledge through 'participatory action and learning' resulted into more equitable access to decision making and benefits sharing. This became possible because PAL contributed towards creating an environment conducive to bringing diverse perspectives, interests, knowledge and information from within and beyond the community into discussion.

Knowledge related to natural resources and their management is stored in the mind and means of so many stakeholders and institutions, and in formal and informal ways that it is, ideally, hard to assess the legitimacy and dominancy of knowledge of one individual or knowledge communities to others. That is where the rationale for democratising and co-creating knowledge is justified. When stakeholders with diversity of interests, knowledge and power interact and collectively learn it is likely that there would be a synergy to develop social practices for the management and use of natural resources. Most of the equity outcomes became possible through a series of interactions and negotiations between users (individuals and sub-groups), EC and external facilitators.

Role of external knowledge is also evident in the context where local knowledge and information are valued less by the local people against external ones who hold power and transfer knowledge of group governance and forest management (Banjade 2003). Usually it is observed that the local elites provide knowledge to increase their power since the local institutions and processes are often shaped by the unholy alliance and nexus between local elites and bureaucrats (Nightingale 2005).

Conclusion

Based on the knowledge and power of stakeholders involved in CFUG processes, bottom up decision-making systems can provide spaces for knowledge interface among the stakeholders. PAL is an approach and a set of tools that provide series of reflective, democratic and interactive knowledge interface resulting in more equitable forms of governance in CFUGs. Moreover, creating voices for inclusion of the poor, women and marginalised groups within CFUGs' decision-making and benefit sharing is important for democratising knowledge production and use. Action learning can be a useful process to facilitate the process of knowledge production, dissemination and utilisation in changing the *status quo* by developing leadership and raising critical awareness among the users, particularly the poor and marginalised. In addition, the learning process appeared to be useful in creating and sustaining the forum for collective action so as to actively facilitate the users for the discussion, planning, monitoring, and evaluating the activities and performance of the CFUG committees and users.

The finding suggests that it is essential to know the knowledge and power dynamics of involved stakeholders to produce the synergistic effect from the interaction. Different knowledge communities might have been created and functioning in the processes of community forestry development. The proper communication of those knowledge communities is essential to reflect the local innovation in the policy and to implement the policy appropriately. With the lessons of facilitating participatory action and learning in four communities from hills and Terai, it can be argued that a multi-stakeholder and learning based deliberative interface is necessary at all levels of policy processes to democratise knowledge and power of policy making and implementation.

Without proper democratic processes in place, initiatives of community forestry could not address the persistent inequity and unequal power relations of the societies, rather it contributed in strengthening status quo in many places. To address the issue of inequity within communities, and democratisation of knowledge and power on resource management and social change, critical empowerment services to the members of poor and disadvantaged groups are needed. Since democratisation essentially entails a political process, there are likely tensions and condensations during redefining power relationships.

Since knowledge in a society is produced and developed through the interaction of social agents including individuals, interest groups and external agencies, the role of external agents is crucial in challenging local inequity and enabling deliberative spaces in a particular community. In other words, when facilitating agents are adequately equipped with the knowledge and skills of local practice of knowledge creation and application, it would help in democratising local processes and knowledge which can give better outcomes in the form of pro-poor governance, social justice and environmental sustainability. However, the reflective and critical investigation approach for social interactions with deliberation on the learning outputs is a crucial prerequisite in creating emancipatory knowledge at all levels.

References

Banjade, M.R. (2003). *Local Perception and Use of Information for Forest User Groups – a Comparative Case Studies in Dhankuta District, Nepal.* MSc Thesis. The Netherlands: Wageningen University and Research Centre (WUR).

Banjade, M.R. (2006). Transforming Policies and Institutions in Community Forestry of Nepal: The Role of Participatory Action Research. Workshop on *Exploring Regional CBNRM Policy and Policy Advocacy.* The Philippines: International Institute of Rural Reconstruction (IIRR).

Banjade, M.R., N.T. Timsina, H.R. Neupane, T. Bhattarai and S. Rana (2006). Transforming Agency and Structure as an Innovation for Facilitating Pro-poor Governance in Community Forestry in Nepal. *Journal of Forest and Livelihood,* 5 (1): 22–33.

Banjade, M.R.; H. Schanz, and C. Leeuwis (2006). Discourses of Information in Community Forest User Groups in Nepal. *International Forestry Review,* 8(2): 229–240.

Barraclough, S. L. and Ghimire, K. B. (1995). *Forest and Livelihoods: The Social Dynamics of Deforestation in Developing Countries.* London: MacMillan Press Ltd.

Chhetri, R. B. (1999). The Rhetoric and Realities of People's Participation in Conservation and Development in Nepal: An Anthropological Perspective. In R. B. Chhetri and O. P. Gurung (eds.), *Anthropology and Sociology of Nepal: Cultures, Societies, Ecology and Development* (pp. 192–211). Kathmandu: Sociological/ Anthropological Society of Nepal (SASON).

Cooke, B. and U. Kothari (2001). 'The Case for Participation as Tyranny.' In B. Cook and U. Kothari (eds.), *Participation: The New Tyranny* (pp. 1–15). London and New York: Zed.

Hartando, H., M.C. Lorenzo, C. Valmores, L. Arda-Minas, D.M. Burton and R. Prabhu (2003). *Learning Together: Responding to Change and Complexity to Improve Community Forests in the Philippines.* Indonesia: CIFOR.

Hobley, M. (1987). *Involving the Poor in Forest Management: Can it be Done?* The Nepal Australia Project Experience, Network Paper 5c (pp. 1–16). London: Overseas Development Institute.

Hobley, M. (1996). 'The Four Ages of Indian Forestry: Colonialism, Commercialism, Conservation, Collaboration.' In: M. Hobley (ed.) *Participatory Forestry: The process of Change in India and Nepal*, London: Overseas Development Institute. pp. 25–64.

Malla Y, R. Barnes, K. Paudel, A. Lawrence, H. Ojha and K. Green (2002). *Common Property Forest Resource Management in Nepal: Developing Monitoring System for Use at Local Level.* Reading and Kathmandu: The University of Reading and ForestAction.

Malla, Y. B. (1999). 'Tree Management and Household Strategies in a Changing Rural Economy: Beyond the Use of Direct Incentives.' In D.W Sanders, P. C. Huszar, S. Sombatpanit and T. Enters (eds.), *Incentives in Soil Conservation: From Theory to Practice* (pp. 85–99). New Delhi: Oxford and IBH Publishing Ltd.

Malla, Y. B. (2000). 'Impact of Community Forestry Policy on Rural Livelihoods and Food Security in Nepal', *Unasylva*, 51: 37–45.

Malla, Y. B. (2001). Changing Policies and the Persistence of Patron-Client Relations in Nepal: Stakeholders' Response to Changes in Forest Policies. *Environmental History*, 6 (2): 287– 307.

Neupane, H. R. 2000. *Factors that Influence Poorer Households' Access to Forest Products from Community Forests: an Analysis of Forest Management and Benefit Sharing Processes.* MPhil thesis. Reading, UK: The University of Reading.

Nightingale 2005. The Experts Taught Us All We Know: Professionalisation and Knowledge in Nepalese Community Forestry. *Antipode*, 37 (3): 581–604.

Ojha, H., B. Pokhrarel, C. McDougall and K. Paudel (2003). Learning to Govern: How to Improve Monitoring System in Community Forestry in Nepal? *Journal of Forest and Livelihood*, 2 (2): 23–34.

Ojha, H., B. Pokharel, K. Paudel and C. McDougall (2002). *Stakeholder Collaboration, Adaptive Management and Social Learning: a Comparative Review of Eight Community Forestry Sites in Nepal.* Kathmandu and Indonesia: ForestAction and CIFOR.

Ojha, H., N. Timsina and D. Khanal (2007). How are Forest Policy Decisions Made in Nepal. *Journal of Forest and Livelihood*: 6 (1) pp. 1–17.

Paudel, K. and H. Ojha (2002*). A Review of Monitoring Systems and Practices in Community Forestry at Local Level.* Kathmandu and Indonesia: ForestAction and CIFOR.

Pokharel, B. K. (1997). *Foresters and Communities in Contention and Compact: A Case of Community Forestry in Nepal.* PhD Thesis. Norwich, UK: University of East Angila.

Timsina, N. P. (2002). *Political Economy of Forest Resource Use and Management: An Analysis of Stakeholders' Interests and Actions in Nepal's Community Forest Management.* PhD Thesis. Reading, UK: The University of Reading.

Timsina, N. P. (2003). Promoting Social Justice and Conserving Montane Forest Environments: A Case Study of Nepal's Community Forestry Program. *The Geographical Journal,* 169 (3): 236–242.

7

Culturally Embedded Knowledge in Irrigation: People's Ways of Thriving in a Himalayan Village

Ram B Chhetri

Introduction

In most parts of Nepal today local communities are recognised as the key stakeholders in the conservation and development initiatives and outcomes in relation to natural resource management including water and forests. The local communities which are recognised as Users Groups have been instrumental in managing such resources either through an indigenous and/or traditional management system or through their involvement in externally sponsored initiatives. Irrespective of the type of system in place for the management and development of natural resources, local communities have demonstrated by means of their efforts that combining local knowledge and initiatives with external knowledge and inputs can be beneficial for all (for illustrations see Fisher 1989; Chhetri 1993; Chhetri and Pandey 1992). By now, local communities or Users Groups have gained fame as extremely competent and knowledgeable managers of natural resources.

Locally gained (through an iterative learning process) and shared knowledge about natural resources, environmental and climatic features, etc., have allowed many communities in Nepal to thrive in all kinds of geographical locations including the Himalayan regions. The *Loba* of upper Mustang are one such people. This paper, based on a study[12] in Lo Manthang examines how the *Loba* people have managed water and other critical resources essential for making a living in a high altitude desert-like area lying behind the Annapurna and Dhaulagiri Himalayan ranges in north-western Nepal. Since the area lies in the rain shadow, managing water from the snow-fed streams (coming down from the surrounding mountains) for various purposes is of critical importance for the survival of local people. Any observer visiting this area today would agree that almost none of the human settlements in upper Mustang would have been there if, to start with, people had not built and operated the irrigation systems by harnessing water from the snow-fed streams. This is certainly true of Lo Manthang (present study site) as well as most of the villages lying in the northern part of Mustang district.

The observation that villages in upper Mustang would not be there without local irrigation systems has a conceptual affinity to Karl Wittfogel's 'hydraulic hypothesis' wherein he posited that under certain circumstances, the imperatives of building and operating large-scale irrigation system could result in increased political integration and then state formation (Wittfogel 1956). Steward incorporated this hypothesis into a broader evolutionary framework to explain the origins of the first state-level societies in a number of places including the Central Andes, Egypt and Mesopotamia (Steward 1955). Attempts to test this hypothesis as a cross-cultural generalisation have led to two divergent positions, viz., a contention that a positive correlation is to be found between centralised political authority and large scale irrigation; and an argument that a centralised control and coordination need not necessarily

---

12 The information for this paper largely comes out of an ethnographic research carried out among the *Loba* people of upper Mustang in the early 1980s. Information on the irrigation system was updated in 2004.

be an imperative for irrigation (for details see Sidky 1997). The present case study of indigenous irrigation management system in Lo Manthang was not undertaken to test the hydraulic hypothesis. However, it appears that the observations and arguments emerging from this study do remind us of that hypothesis. For instance, the control of irrigation system in Lo Manthang by the *Kuthag* families (who belong to the clan of the Raja of Lo) is perhaps an indication that the building and operating of the irrigation system here was initiated by their ancestors in order to consolidate their control over the local villages and their resources.

Lo Manthang was selected as the study site for looking at the indigenous management system of irrigation in the Himalayan region of Nepal[13]. There were some reasons for selecting this site for the present study. First, the author had already collected some information on irrigation and farming practices in Lo Manthang more than 20 years ago. This village presents one of the rare examples of indigenous irrigation management systems operating without much external support or inputs in the Himalayan region of the country. Closer links were observed among the local socio-political organisations, farming activities, village rituals and the irrigation system in Lo Manthang presented as a unique case for exploration. Given this, it was felt that a more focused study on the irrigation system would allow a better understanding of the *Loba* people and their culture. Finally, the fact that it lies in the rain shadow of the mountainous region of Nepal and how people adapt in such harsh environmental conditions was considered as a very important research question by itself.

In Lo Manthang, the local villagers have an irrigation system built and managed by themselves without much technical or social support from outside. Due to the arid and dry climatic conditions prevailing in this part of Mustang district, agriculture and other farming activities

---

[13] Doing research Lo Manthang is not that easy. Arriving there and living in the village located at an elevation of about 13,000 feet above sea level can be a challenge in itself. The quickest way to travel to Lo Manthang today is to catch a flight to Jomsom (the district headquarters of Mustang) from Pokhara and then walk from there for 3-4 days (depending on one's stamina for negotiating distances in high altitude trails).

could not be imagined without a robust irrigation system in place. The indigenous irrigation system under study in Lo Manthang is already few hundred years old and until recently, there have been no external inputs into the system. It has been learnt from this case study that people in this very remote location have been able to build a knowledge system and pass the accumulated knowledge through locally devised organisations and ritual activities. The traditional socio-political organisation (led by the *Kuthag* households) at the village level has been instrumental in not only managing the irrigation system but also in passing down the appropriate technical[14] and social knowledge to the younger generation for the survival of the community in this harsh environment. This case shows that learning is not confined to the formal domain of life only. Social agents who live as a small community with rich traditions and cultural resources actually promote learning and innovations as part of their life. Therefore, the culturally embedded knowledge about irrigation has enabled the *Loba* people to live and thrive in the Himalayan village of Lo Manthang. The empirical information and the analysis of it presented in this chapter points to the fact that combination of 'technical/scientific knowledge' of the experts and 'indigenous/traditional knowledge' of the villagers/farmers can often help us obtain better results in the management of natural resources like irrigation water.

The chapter is based on information collected in 1983–1984 and 2004. Some of the contextual information comes out of the field study conducted by the author in 1983–1984 while doing an ethnographic research in Lo Manthang as a member of the Mustang Integrated Research Programme[15].

Lo Manthang irrigation system: Social and cultural setting

Lo Manthang village lies in upper Mustang. It is located on the southern end of the Tibetan plateau in the trans-Himalayan region of the upper

---

[14] Indigenous knowledge too contains its own technological knowledge. The use of the term 'technical' is to acknowledge this reality.

[15] This research was managed by the Research Centre for Nepal and Asian Studies, Tribhuvan University and funded by IDRC, Canada.

Kali-Gandaki valley in north-western Nepal. The Annapurna and Dhaulagiri mountain ranges separate Mustang from the other Himalayan regions of Nepal. Lo Manthang is located at an elevation of 3800 metres above sea level. The border between Nepal and Tibet is just a few hours walking distance away from here. Today Lo Manthang is linked with Tibet by a motorable dirt road.

The upper Mustang region does not get much rain during the monsoon period in Nepal. So, agriculture here can not depend on rain water. In this dry and arid region, life would be impossible without the glacial streams that intersect the landscape. Two streams known locally as Dhokpo Lho and Dhokpo Zhang (these are in fact the sources of the Kali Gandaki River) which pass through the north and south of Lo Manthang (both river beds are at least 100 metres deeper than the flat plane on which the walled settlement and the farmlands surrounding it are located). These two streams supply most of the water needed by the *Loba* of Lo Manthang for irrigation, drinking, washing, running water-powered grinding mills, and for running the recently constructed micro-hydro power plant. The region is practically a high altitude desert. However, the two snow-fed streams and other water bodies including human controlled water flows (i.e., irrigation) have created oases here and these and around the settlements.

The people in the region identify themselves as *Loba*. They are culturally inclined towards Tibet. Although they are Buddhists (mostly followers of the Shakyapa sect) they are divided into hierarchical social groups known locally as *Kuthag*, *Phlawa* and *Ghara*. These groups normally practice endogamy while exogamous unions between the *Kuthags* and *Phalwas* are not uncommon these days. At the time of field study in 2004, there were a total of 162 households in Lo Manthang with a total population of 857 (419 male and 438 female). In terms of population composition by caste/ethnic group, the *Phalwa* consisted of about 72 per cent while *Kuthags* and *Gharas* each had about 14 per cent of the total population in Lo Manthang. The *Kuthag* people belong to the ruling class in the Lo region and they often equate themselves with the *Bista* (a Chhetri sub-group). Similarly, the *Phalwa* present themselves as similar to the *Gurung* ethnic groups while the *Ghara* consist of smiths, tailors/musicians, butchers, etc. These social groups and their numeric strength (population size) in Lo Manthang become relevant when we discuss the socio-political and cultural dimensions of the irrigation system in detail.

The main village of Lo Manthang is a walled settlement – resembling a fort surrounded by a wall which stands as tall as 26 feet. There is one big main entrance to the walled settlement. The *Kuthags* and *Phalwas* are the main resident inside the walled settlement. The *Gharas* live in a hamlet outside the wall of Lo Manthang situated on a lower plane down by the banks of a local stream called Dhokpo Lho. The village on the banks of this stream is also considered as part of the Lo Manthang settlement.

One special feature of this part of Nepal is that there is a local Raja recognised as a petty king by the government of Nepal. The Raja belongs to the *Kuthag* group of *Loba* people. His territory consists of a locally recognised area called Lo Chho Dhwin (literally meaning the seven areas of Lo) which comprises about 20 or more villages today in the northern half of Mustang district. Besides the Raja, the Buddhist Monks and the monastic institutions are also to be reckoned influential in matters related to life and order in the villages.

Irrigation practices and the role of indigenous knowledge

The interrelationship between local culture, environment and indigenous knowledge on irrigation will be discussed in this section. In doing this, the focus will be on the perceptions of the local people on their environment and resources (cosmos) and how these are reflected in their behaviour and practices. The discussion will cover a number of aspects including the local socio-political organisation in place for managing irrigation related works such as the undertaking of irrigation related tasks, the *Loba* people's perception of their natural world and resources like water, local myths and beliefs on irrigation and agriculture, and the rituals involving the use of water resources.

In Lo Manthang, just as in the Central Andes (see Guillet 1987), the management of water is in the hands of the local socio-political organisation. This body constitutes a *Ghemba* – the village headman – who is chosen from among the *Kuthag* household heads for an annual term. In fact, the *Kuthag* households in Lo Manthang (except the Raja's) have been assuming this role in rotation. The *Ghemba* is assisted by two *Mithwis* (these are his lieutenants, one nominated by the Raja and the other appointed by the *Ghemba* himself from among the *Phalwas*) and six *Chhyumes* (water watchers). The regular maintenance and repair work of the irrigation system – the main canal – is the responsibility of the whole village. The amount of labour contributions, with some exceptions, is proportional to the amount of land owned by a household. Canal maintenance and starting the local agricultural cycle are preceded by performing religious rituals – reflecting the local belief system regarding cosmology. The cosmos for the *Lobas* constitute humans, the tangible objects in nature as well as the invisible forces reckoned to be part of the nature (both deities and demons). Appeasing deities and warding off the evil spirits from the village are equally critical for an orderly existence and continuation of life and related activities. Initiation of any kind of activity – travel, construction work, etc., is prefaced by a *Temdi* (to do *Temdi* is like wishing good luck).

Indigenous/contextual knowledge is valued. The elderly who may not be able to perform physical labour are also accepted as 'labourers'. They supervise on the site of repair and maintenance work while also sharing their own experience-based knowledge on the irrigation system consisting of not just technical details but also on the ritual, social, cultural and historical facets (and their significance). This could be regarded as a way of 'schooling' or socialisation – i.e., a method of passing down the 'science' from one generation to the next. Sharing of their actual experiences and knowledge gained by observation (iterative learning plus all that they themselves inherited from their elders) over the years is valued as critical for the 'total system' (the irrigation system, the village, farming, livestock health, etc.) to thrive in the harsh environment.

Life in Lo Manthang follows the seasonal rhythms of nature. Maintenance of canals begins in late March/early April – just before planting is to be done. In March-April the frozen soil begins melting – the moisture thereby making it easier to dig and remove rocks that may have fallen into the canal during the winter months. The soil would be damp and thus can be easily packed into canal walls. Once the irrigation water is directed into the canal from the source, walls may collapse initially in a number of places. *Chhyumes* fix such small damages while large collapses call for a mobilisation of communal labour (labour contributions from all stakeholders). The repair work starts from the point of distribution of irrigation water and moves upwards towards the source.

Irrigation and farming practices

Villagers have a simple logic that the amount of snowfalls during the winter determines the volume of water for them in the local streams during the farming season. If the *Lobas* perceive that they may get less water for irrigation during any farming season, they revealed that they put emphasis on planting crops that require less irrigation like naked barley, mustard, buckwheat and potato. Wheat and peas are the other crops that have been cultivated in this region for generations. Besides, in order to optimise the production from the fields, the *Lobas* tend to grow crops in rotation in any given field. For instance, if they cultivate wheat or naked barley in a given plot of farm one year, they would grow buckwheat or mustard the following year. The main crops grown in Lo Manthang and their growing period along with the number of times irrigation required is summarised in Table 7.1. The actual planting times for crops are also determined by the arrival of certain migratory birds in the area.

Table 7.1 Crops and their growing periods in Lo Manthang with irrigation requirements

Crops	Planting Month	How often to irrigate	Harvesting Month
Wheat	March – April	6 times	October – November
Naked barley	March – April	6 times	September – October
Buckwheat	April – May	4 times	September – October
Peas	April – May	4 times	September – October
Mustard	April – May	3 times	September – October
Potato	March – April	Not defined	September – October

Source: Field Survey 2004

Water allocation

Water allocation and turns for irrigation are determined during the Sakaluka ritual. For some of the fields the turn for irrigation is determined by means of a local game called *Para* (in principle it resembles a lottery method). In most cases, the head end farms get the first turn followed by the middle and the tail end farms within the command area of a given canal or sub-canal. Every crop needs irrigation in Lo Manthang. Farmers have, through years of experience, a clear knowledge about the priority and the number of times they have to irrigate each of the crops they grow in their farms. For instance, the farms allocated for peas cultivation get priority for initial irrigation since such fields need to be irrigated before even sowing the seeds.

Farmers have also figured out which crops need more or less intensive inputs including irrigation. Wheat, naked barley have to be irrigated at least six times each from the time of plantation to when the crops are ready for harvest. Similarly, peas and buckwheat need four rounds of irrigation at different intervals while mustard needs to be irrigated only three times. They even have names for the different rounds of irrigation by types of crops. For instance, in the case of peas the first, second, third and fourth irrigation rounds are known as '*Taptsu*' (irrigation before sowing), '*Bhutsu*' (after germination), '*Ngutsu*' (flowering time) and '*Rhezu*' (before ripening). Similar terms are used for the irrigation rounds for wheat and other main crops. For wheat and other crops, '*Khanju*' (after sowing but prior to germination) is considered important.

Maintenance and operation

Maintenance (cleaning and repair of damages) of the irrigation system is done every year in order to ensure smooth and efficient water acquisition, allocation and distribution. The maintenance work begins in March-April soon after the winter sojourners return home (a household census undertaken in 2004 revealed that only 14.8 per cent of the people stayed full time in the village during the previous year). The repair and maintenance work also marks the beginning of farming season (crops are planted by April-May and have to be harvested by early October – just before the onset of winter).

When the repair and maintenance work is begun at the main system of the canals, each and every household (irrespective of whether the household uses the water for irrigation or not) is required to contribute free labour for at least one day. This is because the water from the main canal is also used by the village for drinking, washing etc. Therefore, all villagers are responsible for this main system. But in branch canals, only those farmers having field in the command area of a given canal need to contribute the required labour.

The *Ghemba* determines the day to begin the maintenance work and a day before the onset of the work the *Chhyume* goes around the streets of the village announcing that every household should send a labour for the work. Elderly people also come to the work site and share their knowledge and experiences with the youths but normally there is an age limit (for both men and women) for participating in the canal work – one has to be at least 16 years old. Generally people who are over 60 years of age are not required to work as labourers.

The Sakaluka ritual

This ritual is performed once every year soon after the celebration of the Tibetan new year. The term *Sakaluka* literally means opening the mouth of the earth/soil. The farm deity (locally called Lu – a snake god) is believed to become active at this time and needs to be propitiated. No farming activities including the repair and maintenance of irrigation canals, water storage ponds and ditches should be done before this ritual is performed. The following are required for this ritual:

- The executive committee (new *Ghemba*, two *Mithwis* and six *Chhyumes* selected on this day).
- A pair of *dZos* (local bull that is hybrid of yak and cow).
- A girl to do the ploughing and a boy to broadcast the seeds while pulling the *dZos*.
- A goat to be offered to the deity (freed – not sacrificed).
- A boy to dig manure or compost.
- A girl to put the compost into the basket.
- A boy to dig the canal.
- A girl to remove sands and gravels (dirt) from the canal.
- A lama to read religious verses.
- A Nyngmapa Lama to perform the ritual and puja.

Each and every task is supposed to begin at an auspicious moment determined by the local astrologer. The boys and girls are also selected on the basis of astrological calculations. They start the ceremony by wearing new and traditional clothes and ornaments. The ritual farm activities are performed in the fields of the Raja, of the Monastery and then in one of the local villager's farmland. People also re-establish the field-deity symbolised by a rock (locally called *LhaTho*). The field-deity is called *Lumo kamu*. The *Loba* people believe that water-deity lives at the source of water and she comes down to their field with irrigation water. Therefore, people are sent to do *'puja'* at the site of the canal just before starting agricultural activities and repairing irrigation canals.

So the *Sakaluka* ritual precedes any kind of farm activities in Lo Manthang. At this ritual the officials of the socio-political organisation are changed. On this day, the newly elected *Ghemba* and his associates also determine the turn for irrigation for the coming agricultural season.

This *Sakaluka* ritual is an important event fulfilling both (propitiating deities) humanely and mundane responsibilities. In this harsh mountain environment the power of nature is to be acknowledged and submission rather than challenge seems to be the chosen way to go. The cosmic or supernatural as well as human agencies are put in place (selection of new *Ghemba* and his lieutenants and reinstalling the field shrine Lhatho of Lu) – a renewal of their space, authority and salience in the annual cycle of life and activities in the village. They reaffirm their faith in Lu and in its power to steer natural events for the locals.

The event signifies that the power of the invisible force – the supernatural – is acknowledged. Karma – the efforts put by people to appease deities – are implicitly held responsible for success or failures in crops. Failure is often rationalised by blaming it on any shortcoming in ritual or misconduct or disrespect inadvertently displayed towards the deity by one or more of the fellow villagers. The line between fatalism and Buddhism tends to get hazy at such points.

Local myths

There are some interesting local myths in relation to farming and irrigation. One of them involves a mythical *Mheme* (*Loba*: Grandfather) who is said to have secured enough water rights for Lo Manthang from a source shared with the nearby village of Tso Nhub. The *Mheme* is believed to have tricked the other villager to accept that the water from Lho Ghayakar (one of the sources of Lo Manthang's irrigation water) was actually also going to another stream called Numa Ghung (one that falls within Tso Nhub). He had to put red clay in the source of Lho Ghyakar first and then by tricking the other villagers put some at the source of the other stream too in order to make a point that the water from the former source did flow from under the ground to the source of the other stream. From that time on, it is believed that the people of Lo Manthang have been using the water from Numa Ghung also for irrigation. The *Mheme* is remembered by performing a ritual (and offering tobacco/cigarettes because of a belief that he liked to smoke) at the time of annual repair work of the irrigation system.

There is also a belief prevalent in the village that the water in the canal becomes impure and poisonous during the winter months. An eagle is believed to put poison in the water and its use during the winter is believed to cause skin diseases (mainly cracking of the skin in the hands and feet). The water is also considered harmful for the livestock. This water in the canal is believed to be purified only after another migratory bird (locally known as *Jsyakhun-Ghyau* meaning the king bird) comes and touches it at the end of the winter season. In fact, by the time this bird arrives in the area, the water in the canals would have melted and become warm also.

Interface between local and scientific systems of knowledge

The irrigation system in Lo Manthang must be as old as the settlement itself. The system, in its physical structure seems to have changed little at least during the past two decades or so. According to the local people, any extension and enlargement of physical system is made only when it is deemed essential. In major construction and repair work each and every farm household is required to make labour contributions as determined by the *Ghemba*. However, the Raja (local king) and some elite households who have rented out their farms are exempt from this mandatory labour contribution. In such cases, the tenants are responsible for making all kinds of contributions for construction and repair work of the irrigation system. Although the Raja and the elite stay away from manual labour, they do value the local knowledge and acquire it through observation and by listening. They tend to concentrate more on control and mobilisation of the people and resources.

The main structures in irrigation system here consist of weir, intake, main canal (*Loba: Hyura*), sub-canals, conduits (wooden or plastic) storage ponds, and other water distribution devices. Use of local technology and locally available materials has been given high priority. The fields in different locations of the command area have different names and some of such names are also used to identify the several irrigation canal systems like Huyu, Suruk, Samzi, Kya-Kya Ghang, Dhurang and Ghayaga. Huyu is the largest system and the water from this is used not just for irrigating the field but also for other purposes (since it passes by the settlement) including household use.

Topography demands that conduits need to be used in some places. In the past *Loba* people used only wooden conduits (although wood had to be transported from outside the area). They also avoided making the canals steeper in order to avoid strong currents and soil erosion. Field observation and discussions with farmers in 2004 revealed that some modern technologies or materials like iron netting wires (Chicken wire), pipes, and cement have been used in some places. Otherwise, in most of the places, local materials and technologies have been used for the physical construction. In very steep areas, walls are constructed by using large boulders and stones. Storage ponds (*Zhiu*) are to be found in various locations. Water outlets and water division devices mostly consist of stone slabs. Rags (*Loba: Ghala*) are used as washers to control leakage and seepage.

The canals from head to tail are carefully constructed and maintained by the farmers. When canals or sub-canals needed to cross deep gullies, they used wooden conduits (*Loba: Ha*) in the past. Today, they have also started using plastic pipes and cement for this purpose. In some places they have also strengthened the canals by constructing cemented structures. Water division devices in canal are made temporarily using locally available materials. Today, some tunnels have also been constructed by using a combination of pipes and cemented slabs. Thus, in recent years there is an attempt to combine modern and local technology in the construction of irrigation canal system.

Some new constructions proposed by engineers sent to Lo Manthang within the past 2-3 decades, by the concerned government agencies, have been found by the *Loba* farmers to be unsuited to the local needs. In fact, such engineers themselves are said to have realised that the local knowledge and technology were better suited to keep the irrigation system strong while meeting the needs of the local farmers. Indigenous knowledge about the ways of constructing, maintaining and managing the irrigation system have been proven more practical.

There was an intake canal construction project supported by District Development Committee, Mustang district in the early 1980s. The engineers came and constructed a cemented canal. However, in undertaking this work, apparently they did not consult the local socio-political organisation and the farmers about the volume of water that the villagers would need in the canal. After the construction work was completed, villagers realised that the canal was too narrow to supply the actual amount of water that needed to flow through the canal. As a result villagers soon decided to break the newly constructed cemented intake canal and then design their own traditional structure. The farmers talk about this project and argue that the cemented canal was not an improvement but a destruction of their locally constructed structure. The loss in this case was perceived to have been the result of external technical experts not paying due regard to local needs as well as locally tested local technological knowledge.

The locals also talk about a second project that was supported by the District for improving the irrigation system. In this case the project tried to replace a fairly large wooden conduit by using plastic pipes. The technical experts from the district headquarters joined the pipe in such a way that the water would first be made to go straight down from one end of the gulley to the bottom and then be forced to flow upwards in order to be delivered into the canal again. In a fragile environment as Lo Manthang where the top soil tends to be loose and sandy, the amount of silt in the water would vary concomitantly with the water current. Soon the sands blocked the pipe at the bottom and the pipe broke. The *Lobas* claim that they had initially suggested that the pipes not be laid in vertical positions. At the end their suggestions had to be followed after the first inputs to improve the structure of the irrigation system failed.

While the locals have rejected some of the externally sponsored knowledge and technologies in relation to their irrigation system, they have accepted the materials that are perceived to have advantage over locally available resources. Thus, the use of cement and plastic pipes has been accepted in strengthening the canals at sites where the constructions with locally available materials have proven unstable. *Loba* people possess knowledge about their environment and the resources therein. Such knowledge has been passed down orally and through actual practice/ demonstration. They have constructed knowledge and developed technologies about local irrigation system from their own experience of years and a process of iterative learning. Only some of the externally provided technological inputs have been incorporated in the local irrigation system. Locals tend to regard their own indigenous knowledge passed down to them by their elders to be more effective and sustainable in irrigation system.

Local knowledge: The interplay with power

As stated above, the turns for irrigation are determined by the *Ghemba* and his team in the local socio-political body. Once the farming activities begin, people also need to take proper care of their livestock – cattle, horses, donkeys, goats and sheep. Any stray cattle found in the farms during the agricultural period is liable to *Tsepa* i.e., a penalty (in cash) determined by the *Ghemba*. It is the *Chhyumes* who are responsible for patrolling and monitoring the agricultural fields and report cases of rule violations as well as any impending damage to the irrigation system. Disputes often occur after everyone has had the third round of their irrigation turn. This is so because after the third round of irrigation (since at least three rounds of irrigation is considered essential for each of the crops) the rule changes 'first come first serve' in using irrigation water. So, often people compete for irrigation water and end up getting into disputes with neighbours.

Decision-making frequently occurs through the local organisation. It is the main body responsible for the management of irrigation system and for enforcing the rules and regulations in farm works. In most cases, villagers have a say in making decisions about irrigation system, and about the amount of *Tsepa* by kinds of violations of rules. The role of both committee members and villagers is equally important in resolving disputes resulting because of rule violations like stealing some ones turn for irrigation etc. However, on most of the day to day activities, the *Ghemba* can make the decisions himself. For instance, he is the one who fixes the date and time for meetings, time for repair/maintenance, about the labor contribution or for special maintenance work. The two *Mithwis* also make some minor decisions. If there is water dispute within a system, they could resolve it by means of mediation. In the serious cases of conflicts (related to irrigation, farm work, property, and household quarrels) the Raja with the help of *Ghemba* gives the final judgment. The other institution that is revered by the *Lobas* and therefore, has a very important role in local decision making, dispute resolution etc., is the Monastery (*Gomba*) and its senior *Lamas*.

Sometimes the farmers in Lo Manthang also seem to have conflicts among different systems and villages in relation to sharing water for irrigation. Such types of conflicts generally are related to sharing the source of water. People report that conflicts over sharing water are frequent between Lo Manthang and Kimaling villages. People from both villages tend to claim their rights over the use of water from Kimaling stream although it flows only through Kimaling. Through generations of water sharing practice, they seem to have an agreement that the people of Lo Manthang get the water of Kimaling stream during the night while Kimaling people use it during the day time.

It is interesting to note that the elected representatives of local government do not seem to be given any roles, responsibilities and authority in undertaking village level development works, in making decisions or in resolving disputes. Similarly, women and *Ghara* people too seem to hardly have any involvement in such work. In fact, *Ghara* people are not even allowed to be members in the traditional socio-political organisation.

Conclusion

It is clear from the discussion above that the local community in Lo Manthang has thrived in a harsh environment by means of their indigenous and traditional knowledge accumulated and passed down orally through generations. Indigenous knowledge and skills have been the basis for a sustainable irrigation management in Lo Manthang. This supports the idea that local knowledge about the environment and resource therein and the use of such knowledge promote the sustainability of development. This of course does not mean that external scientific knowledge is not useful. On the contrary, the observed reality suggests that locals have found it more meaningful to adopt external technical inputs and adapt them to the local conditions. This only suggests that an effective dialogue between the external experts (engineers in the present case) could forge an interface between the two knowledge systems and thereby promote locally appropriate development.

Institutional arrangements are made by (local) people in order to manage the vital and scarce water resource. Complex power relations and power structures could be discovered in situations requiring careful management of scarce water resources for irrigation and other purposes. Institutional arrangements may consist of: organisations, established set of rules for regularising behaviour, sanctions for violations of rules (customary or otherwise), religious rituals; definition of rights to resource (the amount plus the fact that whether once can access or not). All of these are very much part of the social and cultural fabric of Lo Manthang.

Studies focusing on the relationship between irrigation system and power structure have shown the existence of a two-way relationship: irrigation system reflect the existing power structure (in Lo Manthang the *Ghemba* cannot be other than a *Kuthak*) through distribution of benefits and obligations, and the dynamics of irrigation system influence power relations by either reproducing or transforming prevailing societal relationships. This study in Lo Manthag corroborates the general trend. The *Kuthak* elite and the *Raja* have held the power and remain key players in local decision making in the irrigation and development related matters which suggest that the traditional power relations continues on. When and how will this change? This remains an open question for future research.

Irrigation water management system of Lo Manthang is independent from the central authority in the country. For instance, the *Ghemba* in Lo Manthang is not a part of formal government body and is not linked to state's authority either. However, it has to be acknowledged that only the local elite consisting of *Kuthag* families hold major public decision making positions. Female and *Ghara* in particular are excluded from participation in such decision making.

A policy conclusion that emerges out of this case study is that any development project which ignores local knowledge and advice can falter and fail; it can also be rejected by the locals as inappropriate work. True participation of locals and a genuine regard and use of local knowledge system (i.e., a true dialogue between so called science and local knowledge) in resource management is the proper way to go. This again is not to suggest that local knowledge is adequate by itself. In fact, this case study on indigenous system of irrigation in Lo Manthang corroborates a statement made by R Chambers (Chambers1983) that local knowledge and scientific knowledge when combined may achieve what neither could do on its own.

This study also allows us to conclude that culturally devised strategies and arrangements which have been working in difficult environments should not be replaced by external agents with supposedly better technical solutions. The community knowledge accumulated through generations of iterative learning is embedded in local culture including rituals, organisations, and norms. Such knowledge may have the potential to supplement and complement the external technical knowledge. One only needs receptive eyes and ears to discover their value and act accordingly.

Acknowledgement

I would like to thank Tunga Rai who accompanied me to Lo Manthang and agreed to undertake his M.A. thesis research on the irrigation system there. I appreciate his support in collecting the household level data in 2004.

References

Chambers, R. 1983. *Rural Development: Putting the Last First*. New York: Longman Scientific and Technical.

Chhetri, R.B. and T.R. Pandey (1992). *User Group Forestry in the Far-Western Region of Nepal. Case Studies from Baitadi and Achham*. Kathmandu: ICIMOD.

Chhetri, R.B. (1993). Indigenous Systems of Forest Protection and Management in the Far Western Hills of Nepal, In D. Tamang, G.J. Gill, and G.B. Thapa (eds.), *Indigenous Management of Natural Resources in Nepal* (pp. 323–342). Kathmandu: Government of Nepal- Ministry of Agriculture/Winrock International

Fisher, R.J. (1989). Indigenous Systems of Common Property Forest Management in Nepal. *Environment and Policy Institute* (EAPI) Working Paper No. 18. Honolulu, HI: EAPI, East-West Center.

Guillet, D. (1987). Terracing and Irrigation in the Peruvian Highlands, *Current Anthropology*, 24 (4): 409–430.

Sidky, H. (1997). Irrigation and the Rise of State in Hunza: A Case for the Hydraulic Hypothesis. *Modern Asian Studies*, 31 (4): 995–1017.

Steward, J.H. (1955). *Irrigation Civilizations: A Comparative Study*. Washington, D.C.: Pan American Union.

Wittfogel, K.A. (1956). Hydraulic Civilisations, In Jr. William Thomas (ed.), *Man's Role in Changing the Face of the Earth* (pp. 152–164). Chicago: University of Chicago Press.

8

Deliberative Knowledge Interface: Lessons and Policy Implications

Hemant R Ojha, Krishna P Paudel,
Netra P Timsina and Ram B Chhetri

Introduction

A question that guided the research project as well as the process of editing the book has been: how different systems of knowledge operate around natural resource governance, and how different categories of social agents associated with different systems of knowledge engage in the process of deliberation. Our aim was to bring together empirical evidence and theoretical insights to explore and substantiate key issues and innovations, as well as to draw policy lessons in relation to enhancing deliberative interface among diverse knowledge systems that exist in the context of natural resource governance. We drew upon critical, theoretical insights of French sociologist Pierre Bourdieu (mainly practice, habitus and field) and German political theorist Jürgen Habermas (mainly communicative reason and deliberation) for the empirical analysis of six case studies of natural resource management in Nepal. The case studies are representative of the various sub-sectors of natural resource governance such as forest, water and agriculture in Nepal at local, sub-national and national levels. These cases together present diverse situations of interface among various systems of knowledge.

The six case studies confirm our proposition (see Chapter one) that effective natural resource governance in Nepal is heavily influenced and shaped by the processes through which different categories of social agents and their respective systems of knowledge interact and deliberate with one another. The empirical materials presented in the chapters amply demonstrate that all situations of natural resource governance, to varying degrees, reflect a deliberative interface among four categories of social agents, namely: civil society, techno-bureaucrats, formal politicians and development agencies. While one can identify specific class-differentiated sub-groups within these categories, it was found that the four groups represent epistemological differentiation in relation to governance. In other words, these groups of agents nurture and are nurtured by relatively distinct systems of knowledge which underpin their political positions, perspectives and competence, with regard to negotiating rules and practices of governance.

Four systems of knowledge and perspectives

When seen from Bourdieu's theory of practice, we found that practices of natural resource governance are shaped by four categories of deep-seated and reproducible cultural dispositions/mindsets (or doxa) nurtured in Nepalese society. These doxas are practiced by different human agencies or habitus. First, there is a large group of people commonly known as forest officials, foresters, agricultural scientists, engineers, rangers, overseers, technical specialists and so on who work in government, administrative and technical services. They all share a common technocratic habitus, which emphasises technical strategies of forest management at the expense of creating accountable and deliberative institutions of resource governance and benefit sharing. Social agents with this doxa insist that forest management is a technical matter and expert analysis and prescriptions should be the prime basis of decision-making, planning and organising governance practices.

The six case studies represent different groups of people who practice technical doxa in natural resource governance. The case of forest inventory is in part a story about how scientific forestry experts enacted their technical doxa in community forestry at the levels of policy and practice. In the case of NARC, agricultural scientists enact technical doxa which is reflected in their commodity focused research without paying adequate attention to socio-economic factors that affect access of the poor farmers to improved technology and agricultural inputs. Agricultural scientists are primarily divided according to commodities, and research is organised with a goal of enhancing productivity, not equity. *Chhattis Mauja* and Lo Manthang demonstrate a situation where irrigation engineers have come into interface with local people, albeit to lesser extent. In the context of FECOFUN and community forestry, the case studies indicate continuing civil society efforts to transform technical doxa of forest officials.

Second, development NGOs and donor projects exert significant influence over natural resource governance. They share developmental or *vikase* habitus as they consider social engineering a model of change – programmed and projected methods of social interactions, ordering people in formal groups, emphasising planned activities and creating external dependencies. They have a limited sense of need to explore how more deliberative processes of restructuring and transformation can take place so that the direction and agenda of change reflects not only the notions of modernity advocated by outsiders but also the endogenous views of change and progress. In the wider field of development, there is almost a consensus that formal, economically and technologically focussed incremental process of change in the western fashion is the solution to the problem of underdevelopment. In all the cases, the authors report one or the other aspect of deliberative gaps between local and external knowledge systems.

The nature and extent of *vikase* habitus vary in the six case studies. Key institutions of natural resource governance in four cases (except *Chhatis Mauja* and Lo Manthang) are primarily driven by development agencies funded by donor money. The practices and institutions of natural resource governance are in part shaped by underlying *vikase* habitus, but the extent of influence depends on actual status of negotiation between developmental knowledge system and other knowledge systems defined by other groups of social agents. In the case of FECOFUN and community forestry, civil society groups have been able to critically engage with the *vikase* habitus, so as to utilise developmental resources without being co-opted significantly by the former.

Third, people dependent on natural resources and other forest users share a common civil society habitus, in the sense that they are all outside of the government, share a common non-governmental social space (though internally differentiated) and share direct livelihood interests over natural resource governance. The fatalistic doxa nurtured in the field of civil society in Nepal creates an illusion that civil society agents do not have legitimate rights to challenge the status quo and lack capacity to contribute to natural resource governance proactively. In the wider field of civil society, this mindset also means that natural resources are the exclusive preserves of government bureaucrats, and that the civil society agents have to accept whatever is given to them. This sense of limit on choice and freedom in the civil life affects the potential of learning and deliberation of civil society habitus in natural resource governance practices[16].

The six case studies present a diversity of civil society habitus. The case of FECOFUN demonstrates civil society agents utilising civil society perspectives and knowledge, critically reflecting upon, and at times going beyond, the entrenched fatalistic doxa. In *Chhattis Mauja* and Lo Manthang, local people have organised themselves to nurture and utilise traditional knowledge around water resource management. In community forestry, local as well as external civil society activists have worked together to transform governance practices. The cases demonstrate significant differentiation among the civil society groups in terms of their potential to participate in deliberative knowledge interface, depending on the access to knowledge related resources in the field of governance.

---

[16] In the recent years, fatalistic mindset (doxa) in Nepalese civil society field is being challenged through a series of crises and struggles. This kind of challenge to doxa for Bourdieu is periodic – sometimes challenged, other times accepted without questioning.

Finally, politicians share a concern over the matters of state and thus enact a common formal political habitus. In democratic systems, elected political leaders are entrusted with an authority to formulate policies and regulations for governing all walks of social life, including natural resources. However, local politicians in Nepal do not seem to believe that local natural resource governance is a political domain, since they appear to be primarily occupied with the power sharing deals at the state level governance. Even when they are engaged in local natural resource governance, they rely on technocratic habitus to design and enact policies without essential deliberative links with concerned citizen groups. A large part of the activity of formal political habitus is based on feudalistic mindset, which does not appreciate the proposition that politicians should look for active opportunities to deliberate with the groups of people being represented before defining the agenda of change and making political decisions. In Nepal, feudalistic mindset forms the prime basis for the construction of different governance units and practices. As a result, leaders of organisations and groups, whether they be in government or not, exercise tremendous power and privileges when they work for their constituencies, and the people who elect the leaders hardly question the non-deliberative exercise of power by their leaders.

The involvement of politicians is indirect and sketchy in the case studies. In the case of NARC and forest inventory, the politicians endorsed the ideas of techno-bureaucrats. In FECOFUN, politicians have indirectly sought to influence governance of FECOFUN and its agenda. In CFUGs, *Chhattis Mauja* and Lo Manthang, the feudalistic mindset of politicians has been a key challenge to deliberative knowledge interface.

Deliberative knowledge interface: Issues and innovations

Issues

Deliberation across diverse domains of knowledge is still limited. However, we have identified a few important deliberative innovations taking place in the field of natural resource governance in Nepal. The analysis of the six case studies suggests that there are a range of cross-cutting and recurrent issues related to deliberation among knowledge systems. These issues are briefly outlined below.

Issues in relation to enhancing deliberation among diverse knowledge systems

- Differences in power, prestige and status among social agents create advantages for some and disadvantages for other knowledge systems.
- Bureaucratic organisations/agents demonstrate significant institutional rigidity to deliberate with citizens in exploring policies and practices of governance.
- Theoretical, generic and reductionist approach of technical specialists do not always go together with the practical, context-specific and problem-oriented perspective of resource user groups.
- There are limited communication and weak information sharing mechanisms.
- There is a monopoly of public institution in production of knowledge.
- There is inadequate recognition of non-governmental research and innovation systems.
- There exists non-transparent alliances of knowledge elites suppressing open deliberation.
- Practices monitoring, reflections and sharing within and between diverse groups of social agents are limited.
- Rhetorical instruments of participatory approach are often used to legitimise non-deliberative processes.

The case studies reveal that resource governance situations are generally dominated by technocratic knowledge systems, and at times, there is reinforcement of feudalistic mindset of politicians, resulting in the exclusion of marginalised groups from the decision making processes. The CFUG case suggests that forest management decisions within community forestry are made by feudalistic habitus of local elites in consultation with technocratic habitus of government forest officials. Of course, there is a substantial degree of negotiation but these two types of dispositions collude to exclude the ordinary and disadvantaged people, who often fail to recognise the subtle exploitative alliance of these two types of agents.

The six cases indicate that large masses of socially marginalised groups (operating within *fatalistic* dispositions), who draw their livelihoods from forest, water and agricultural resources, have actually been deprived of the opportunity as well as legitimacy to participate in deliberative practices. This is one of the reasons why inequitable resource management practices loom large in the field of natural resources in Nepal. The case study of NARC demonstrates that farmers are generally passive recipients of scientific knowledge rather than being an active party in deliberative technological innovations.

Understandably, there has been a proliferation of participatory discourse in development but even this radical notion of change has at times been insufficient to provide unconstrained spaces of deliberation among diverse knowledge systems. In the case of NARC and community forestry inventory, where a strong commitment to participatory approach exists in policy documents and development discourse, social agents with technocratic dispositions have on the contrary, imposed the technical approaches to learning. NARC's research on varietal improvement without concurrent research efforts to understand why poor farmers have limited access to land and agricultural inputs has had limited impact on enhancing the livelihood of the poorest (which is actually the priority of national development policy as stated in the Tenth Five Year Plan and Poverty Reduction Strategy Paper). The inventory policy instrument also sought to impose the ideas of technical forestry as mandatory requirements for forest management within community forestry paradigm, without providing an opportunity to local people to bring in their knowledge systems while defining inventory policy instrument and enacting forest management practices. This was partly due to the high positional power and technical expertise used to disempower local people.

One key aspect in which technical experts and civil society groups differ is the differential emphasis they put on practical and theoretical aspects of learning. The former are guided by theoretical frames and that they rarely appreciate the social dimensions of learning (as in the case of agricultural scientists and foresters in the cases of NARC and forest inventory respectively). On the contrary, local resource users are more guided by practical logic of actions (as in the case of CFUGs, Lo Manthang, and *Chhattis Mauja*). We also identify a distinct group of social agents – critical civil society activists – who have emphasised generative dialogues between theory and practice for learning and change (as in the case of CFUGs with the support from civil society activists).

Our case studies demonstrate a complex dynamics and consequences of learning related inequalities, within and between different categories of social agents. Foresters and forest users have to work in the same field, with varied scopes of access to ideas, information and learning (the cases of inventory and CFUGs). Inequality in knowledge and more importantly the perception of hierarchy because of endowment of knowledge is a barrier to deliberative learning processes. At the community level, elites have wide external networks, and more time to engage in discursive activities, whereas the poor and marginalised groups have to operate within limited scope for learning, reflection and access to outside information (as in the case of Lo Manthang). Knowledge of agricultural scientists and local farmers are given differential weights. In Irrigation, such as *Chhattis Mauja*, the way rich land owning farmers learn or seek to learn (such as construction of big canals, use of technical equipments) is different from small holders, and those who are at the tail end of the canal system. The latter may, as part of their strategy of resistance to the dominant practices, explore and learn how they can violate rules of water uses in the night or at times when others find it difficult to watch. Even within the civil forums like FECOFUN, leaders at central level have substantially greater access to outside information and diverse learning networks, and this is likely to widen inequality between the central leaders and local user groups unless a full-fledged internal democracy is ensured.

Various factors account for poor deliberative interface. First, academic/research institutions are poorly governed creating limited incentives and motivation for creative works. None of the cases in this book report situations of active engagement of such institutions in promoting or facilitating deliberative interface. Second, the role of producing knowledge is confined to public sector institutions that have inherent bottlenecks in fostering innovations (as in the case of NARC and forest inventory). Third, confusion and conflicts prevail in regard to the role of civil society and private sector, as well as their partnership with government institutions, in creating and sharing knowledge. Fourth, there is a weak linkage between policies and practices, limiting knowledge production and communication. The dominant producers of knowledge have limited practice of monitoring the processes and outcomes. Finally, the inherent diversity and differentiation among social agents means that dominant groups are often structurally in better position[17] to create more holistic and legitimate claims of knowledge through more effective allocation of efforts for action and reflection[18]. This is one of the reasons why within forest user group local elites have been able to justify and argue collective decisions in their favour even when the policies and institutions mandate participatory decision-making processes. Given the complex nature of social hierarchy, this raises question as to how democratic deliberation is possible within civil society, and between the civil society and the state. This is critical since without democratic deliberation it is difficult to achieve equitable governance of natural resources.

---

[17] French sociologist Pierre Bourdieu argues that social agents have inherently unequal distribution of opportunities for creating knowledge in any differentiated society, and the ideologies of dominant groups are tacitly accepted by other groups who lack adequate resources to create knowledge. (P. Bourdieu, 1998). Practical reason: on the theory of action. Cambridge, Polity Press).

[18] American pragmatist John Dewey considers knowledge is created when a reflection over an action establishes connection between an action and its consequences (B. Elkjaer, 2003). Social learning theory: learning as participation in social processes. The Blackwell handbook for organisational learning and knowledge management. M. Eastery-Smith and M. Lyles, Blackwell Publishing Ltd.

Innovation

The six case studies presented in this book offer a range of deliberative innovations in knowledge systems interface in the context of natural resource governance in Nepal. These are briefly discussed below.

Key deliberative innovations in natural resource governance in Nepal

- Citizen federations have emerged to challenge techno-bureaucratic domination and to augment civil society perspectives in political deliberation.
- Participatory innovations have been developed to provide some opportunities to farmers to contribute their knowledge in developing improved seeds and varietals selection.
- Critical civil society groups have emerged and are engaged in addressing some of the constraints of marginalised groups to participate in deliberative knowledge interface.
- Deliberative knowledge interface has contributed to the evolution of decentralisation and devolution policies in natural resource governance.
- There are emerging cases of scientific knowledge being used to complement traditional civil society knowledge.
- Effective deliberation between traditional/indigenous knowledge of civil society and the scientific knowledge has resulted in developing more appropriate institutional and technological solutions in governance.

The role of civil society to challenge over-scientisation[19] of the political and social issues is demonstrated by the emergence of FECOFUN. Though the internal learning system within FECOFUN

.[19] The issue of scientisation of political discourses and communicative reason has been a crucial issue in political philosophy following the writings of Jürgen Habermas (R. Roderick, 1986). A particular concern in this regard is that modernist emphasis on technocratic approaches to policy and social change has undermined spaces for political deliberation among ordinary citizens. *Habermas and the Foundations of Critical Theory.* Hampshire and London, Macmillan; J. H. Turner, 1987. *The Structure of Sociological Theory.* Jaipur, Rawat Publications).

is not free from hierarchical influences, the federation as a civil society has been able to challenge the expansion of overly technocratic posture of forest officials in the governance of forest resources. The federation has pooled and organised knowledge systems of ordinary citizens to enhance claims for legitimacy of decentralised and participatory forest management in deliberative interfaces with techno-bureaucrats and politicians. Since local users and marginalised groups are in difficult position to project their views in wider discursive processes, which shape policies, the role of networks such as FECOFUN is critical to bridge such gaps. As a result of a decade long engagement, FECOFUN has demonstrated civil society perspectives of forest governance, while appreciating the useful roles forest science can play when utilised in a deliberative way. Such networking initiatives are also emerging in agricultural and irrigation sectors in Nepal but not so effectively and widely as FECOFUN.

The case of Lo Manthang shows that a system of natural resource governance can exist even without technical and scientific knowledge support. Social agents who live as a small community with rich traditions and cultural resources actually promote learning and innovation as part of their life. This system has been internally deliberative to promote intergenerational transfer of knowledge as well as devise innovative ways to thrive in harsh trans-Himalayan environment. Likewise, the case of *Chhattis Mauja* represents a situation in which civil society knowledge systems has sustained a fairly complex technological infrastructure of irrigation with a command area of several thousand hectares. But in both the situations, there is an increasing sense of receptivity for scientific knowledge to fix some of the continuing technical problems – such as using plastic pipes to pass water across deep gorges in the case of Lo Manthang and using dozer to cleanse sedimentation in the canal floor in case of *Chhattis Mauja*.

Whilst there is evidence suggesting possible positive links between technocratic and feudal legacies, there are instances of critical civil society change agents allying with the marginalised groups, and often forming a critical knowledge link between policy and practice of natural resources management. The case of CFUGs demonstrates a situation in which members of marginalised groups and civil society intellectuals and activists engaged in critical and deliberative processes to empower and transform the fatalistic mindset of marginalised groups. As a result of the deliberative interface between social activists and the marginalised groups, the latter were able to deliberate effectively with local feudal habitus of CFUG leaders and technocratic habitus of forest officials on matters of forest governance. As the authors report, such an improvement in deliberative interface was able to generate more equitable practices of benefit sharing.

We identified persistence of technocratic domination in knowledge interface as a key issue. Yet, there are also instances where technical experts (such as some foresters and agricultural scientists within ForestAction, NARC and Department of Forests) have engaged in challenging the disciplinary presuppositions and are coming out to engage in more deliberative processes and praxis. The case of community forestry inventory indicates how two broadly defined groups – state forest officials and local communities – are in tension over the claim of legitimacy of two contrasting systems of knowledge, local/indigenous and scientific, in the management of community forests as part of the continuing struggle for controlling resources. This analysis leads to the policy frameworks that provide spaces for critical reflection of dominant paradigm and discourses and allow social agents in engaging political dialogues across institutions, groups and stakeholders.

Findings

A key finding of this study is that it is useful to think of natural resource governance as a deliberative interface among four key knowledge systems and the corresponding groups of social agents. Even the processes of policy change can be better understood and facilitated if considered as a deliberative knowledge interface rather than technocratic manipulation. The case studies demonstrate that natural resource governance practices in Nepal present a complex and innovative scenario of governance where diverse knowledge systems come into deliberative interface. However, because of the differential deliberative competencies of different groups of social agents engaged in various systems of knowledge, the deliberative interface is far less effective than it could potentially be.

A common observation through almost all the cases is that learning is incremental rather than transformative[20]. This means that both individuals and institutions hardly explore and question their basic assumptions, 'mental models' – that guide perceptions and methods of knowing. Discursive knowledge is inscribed within a more encompassing cognitive structure, which is seldom challenged. Yet, there are a number of situations in which unquestioned beliefs are challenged and deliberation is enhanced, especially when crises and surprises have begun to appear (such as when water users started changing norms due to demographic compositions in *Chhattis Mauja*).

Because of inherent social inequalities, actors have differential capability to claim, promote and influence their respective knowledge systems. As a result, there is generally a domination of technocratic knowledge and marginalisation of indigenous and traditional knowledge. Current practices of learning are tied to instrumental purposes (of seeking to understand resources, much less people and their relations around resource governance), with limited recognition of critical self-reflexivity and appreciation of dialogical interactions. Uncritical adoption of scientific and *vikase* knowledge has often undermined local civil society knowledge systems which have sustained social life for generations. Civil society's capability to deliberate is enhanced through wider networking and federation. This has also helped to challenge classical techno-bureaucratic doxa and opened up spaces for deliberation.

---

[20] This relates to 'Single Loop Learning' of Chris Argyris (C. Argyris, 1993). On Organisational Learning. Cambridge, MA, Blackwell; Argyris, C. and D. Schön, 1996. Organisational learning II: Theory, method and practice, Reading, Mass, Addison Wesley). Mezirow's theory of transformative learning is even morte relevant from our perspective. E. W. Taylor, 1998. The Theory and Practice of Transformative Learning – A Critical Review. Columbus, Ohio, The Ohio State University.

Conclusion

Our conclusion, however, is not entirely against any technical intervention for change as we have found that unconstrained negotiation and empowered deliberation among diverse systems of knowledge – including local and scientific – can contribute to social learning and democratisation of political institutions. Technical knowledge system should not be rejected even in the participatory context because what is important is deliberation without constraint and imposition. When local civil society groups have ample freedom to evaluate, choose and modify technical/scientific knowledge, there are likelihoods of better resource governance practices.

The notion of indigenous knowledge as a pure domain is problematic as far as understanding governance is concerned. The issue is how civil society groups are internally sustained by knowledge system that enhances civil groups' ability to deliberate with other social agents. The presence of alliance between local elites and state officials around the same domain of knowledge – scientific forestry in determining the nature and quantity of forest harvest – leads us to conclude that the divide between 'indigenous' and 'scientific' knowledge may not exist as sharply distinct as is usually believed, but is very much mediated by local power relations. The implication is that policy framework should provide adequate space for unconstrained deliberation among diverse actors with different knowledge system for social learning and innovations in governance practices.

Mainstream notion of participatory approach to development practice is also problematic as the approach disguises technocratic approaches by defining standards of change through experts. The concept of deliberation can help us see the scope of improvement in the current practice of participatory development. We presented a recent initiative (CFUG action learning) to improve deliberative processes at local level and found that empowerment and mobilisation of marginalised groups, with active facilitation support from civil society activists[21], can allow them to challenge their own doxa (un-reflected and tacitly held beliefs and assumptions), and dominant discourses and narratives, and thus marshal power-knowledge nexus to influence institutional decisions and resource governance practices.

This finding has challenged the initial assumption that institutional frameworks and policies are pre-conditions for development of effective and transformative knowledge systems; it can now be seen that there is significant space for manoeuvring within the existing institutions if social agents start to engage in critical self reflection[22]. This is, however, again related to how the macro policy and institutional environment encourages the development of civil society activism at the grassroots level with a potential for such change. A direction of policy change coming from this lesson is to engage critical civil society activists to challenge fatalistic mindset of marginalised groups and thus empower them to have active dialogue with developmentalist, technocratic and feudal disposition of human agencies. Other specific policy directions emerging from the analysis of the case studies are summarized in below.

Way Ahead

Direction of policy reform to promote deliberative knowledge interface

- Recognise and promote critical civil society agents to address power imbalances in deliberative interface.

---

[21] The role of external agents is contested but we found empirical relevance of Bourdieu's view that human agents on the ground tacitly reproduce the existing social order, and there is a need to provide an epistemological critique, which will bring tacitly held beliefs to discussion and reflection. This resonates with Giddens's view on moving from 'practical consciousness' to 'discursive consciousness', and Dewey's view on the need to bring issues of 'primary experience' into 'secondary experience' of reflection. All these theoretical insights indicate a need for social critique for change, for which critically oriented civil activist and practical researchers have an undeniable role.

[22] This is consistent with Long's emphasis on practice and interaction rather than central policy and planning alone as a source of change. N. Long, 2001. Development sociology; actor perspectives. London and New York, Routledge.

- Recognise multiple knowledge partnerships in research systems in order to develop appropriate institutional and technological innovations.
- Decentralise research systems by recognising and supporting multiple actors of knowledge production.
- Promote a culture of reflection, monitoring, information sharing and deliberation across producers, users and intermediaries.
- Promote networking and federation building among civil society groups including marginalised people.
- Promote research activities that focus on exploring and identifying factors constraining as well as facilitating deliberative knowledge interface.

Research efforts should focus on understanding factors and conditions that facilitates open deliberation among social agents with diverse perspectives and knowledge system on equal footing. Bringing the issue of policy process into public domain beyond the bureaucrats and political representatives may allow better space to widen and deepen civil society actions in democratising knowledge and power relationships. The role of policy makers should be towards enhancing spaces for dialogue and deliberation among concerned social actors while the role of scientists should be to assist informed negotiation of policies.

About the Contributors

Hari R Neupane: Mr Neupane has been involved in the development and implementation of participatory action research methodologies for community forest management and rural livelihoods in Nepal. In this process, he has supported local institutional development and improvement. He is associated with Environmental Resources Institute (ERI) and ForestAction Nepal.
Contact email: **hrn@forestaction.wlink.com.np**

Harisharan Luintel: Mr Luintel has been actively involved in participatory natural resource management since 1988. He is focusing on participatory action research combining local and scientific knowledge systems. He is associated with Environmental Resources Institute (ERI) and ForestAction Nepal.
Contact email: **hl@forestaction.wlink.com.np**

Hemant R Ojha: Dr Ojha has conducted research on various aspects of natural resource governance in Nepal as well as internationally. He has conducted extensive theoretical review on knowledge, power and governance as part of his recent PhD and other related research works. He has published in Journals such as Policy and Society, International Development Planning Review, International Journal of Social Economics, and International Forestry Review. Dr Ojha is the founding member of Environmental Resources Institute (ERI) and ForestAction Nepal.
Contact email: **hojha@wlink.com.np**

Krishna P Paudel: Mr Paudel has recently submitted his PhD thesis entitled 'Knowledge, power and practice in community forestry: a case from Nepal's Terai'. He has been involved in research, advocacy and capacity building in the field of community forestry for more than a decade. He has conducted action research on developing monitoring system, adaptive and collaborative management, and knowledge systems development in natural resource management. Mr Paudel is a founding member of Environmental Resources Institute (ERI) and ForestAction Nepal.
Contact email: **kpp@forestaction.wlink.com.np**

Laya P Upreti: Dr Upreti is the Reader in Anthropology at Tribhuvan University, Nepal. He has also worked as a consultant for the last two decades in different national consulting firms/NGOs/INGOs, agencies of the UN, and bilateral and multilateral organisations. He has co-authored three books, namely, *Critical Webs of Power and Change: A Resource Pack for Planning, Reflection and Evaluation of People–Centered Advocacy (2005); Indian Seasonal Labor Migration into Nepal Terai*, (200) and *The Social Dynamics of Deforestation: A Case Study from Nepal* (1996). He has more than two dozen research articles published in the reputed academic and professional journals. His research interest is primarily in the indigenous knowledge systems for natural resources management.
Contact email: **layaup@mos.com.np**

Mani Ram Banjade: Mr Banjade has recently worked as the Coordinator of ForestAction Nepal. He has extensive experience in community forestry, participatory action research, information (including knowledge and experience) management, action learning initiatives, and in the fields of institutional change. He has designed, planned, implemented and monitored a number of participatory action research projects including adaptive management of community forests in multi-stakeholder environment. He is associated with Environmental Resources Institute (ERI) and ForestAction Nepal.
Contact email: **mrb@forestaction.wlink.com.np**

Netra P Timsina: Dr Timsina's development and research experience encompass diverse aspects of natural resource management within the context of Nepal. His research areas include resource governance and livelihoods, analysis of knowledge and politics in resource management, design and implementation of action research, and networking and alliance building. He is associated with NGO federation of Nepal, Environmental Resources Institute (ERI) and ForestAction Nepal. Contact email: **npt@forestaction.wlink.com.np**

Ram B Chhetri: Dr Chhetri is a Reader in Anthropology at Tribhuvan University. Currently he is the Head of the Central Department of Sociology/Anthropology, Tribhuvan University. He has been a visiting faculty/scholar at the University of Georgia, USA, the University of Bergen, Norway (1995), Chr. Michelsen Institute, Norway and the Institute of Social Studies, The Hague (2005). He has co-authored several books including *User Group Forestry in Far-Western Nepal* (ICIMOD, Kathmandu 1992), *Nepal-Australia Community Forestry Project: Socio-Economic Study* (ANUTECH, Canberra 1996), *Dispute Resolution in Nepal: A Socio-Cultural Perspective* (CVICT, Kathmandu 2004); edited a book: *Changing Environments and Livelihoods in Nepal* (2006, Centre for Nepal and Asian Studies, TU) and co-edited *Anthropology and Sociology of Nepal* (SASON, 1999), *Occasional Papers in Sociology and Anthropology* 9 (Tribhuvan University, 2005). He has also published widely in national and international journals. Contact email: **rbc@forestaction.wlink.com.np**